G000076936

On December 16 1897, WILLIAM TERRISS, one of London's most popular actors was murdered at the Stage Door of the Adelphi. The person most affected, but the least considered at the time, was his Mistress, the young actress, JESSIE MILLWARD. This is their story.

FINAL PERFORMANCE

A true story of Love, Jealousy, Murder and Hypocrisy

Ruth Silvestre.

with best wishes.

RUTH SILVESTRE

Copyright © 2009 Ruth Silvestre

The moral right of the author has been asserted.

Apart from any fair dealing for the purposes of research or private study,
or criticism or review, as permitted under the Copyright, Designs and Patents
Act 1988, this publication may only be reproduced, stored or transmitted, in
any form or by any means, with the prior permission in writing of the
publishers, or in the case of reprographic reproduction in accordance with
the terms of licences issued by the Copyright Licensing Agency. Enquiries
concerning reproduction outside those terms should be sent to the publishers.

Matador
5 Weir Road
Kibworth Beauchamp
Leicester LE8 0LQ, UK
Tel: 0116 279 2299
Fax: 0116 279 2277
Email: books@troubador.co.uk
Web: www.troubador.co.uk/matador

ISBN 978 1848761 445

British Library Cataloguing in Publication Data.
A catalogue record for this book is available from the British Library.

Typeset in 11pt Book Antiqua by Troubador Publishing Ltd, Leicester, UK

Printed in Great Britain by the MPG Books Group, Bodmin and King's Lynn

Matador is an imprint of Troubador Publishing Ltd

*To Tony White who started me on my journey
and to Barry Foster who pointed the way ahead.*

ACKNOWLEDGEMENTS

To the London Library. The Irving Society. And especially to the Mander and Mitchenson Theatre Collection for their encouragement.

To the Staff at the late, lamented Theatre Museum, who chose the dramatic version of 'Final Performance' for a rehearsed reading in the Painted Room. To the cast who generously gave their time and endeavour. Charles Stapley. Miranda Foster. Osmund Bullock. Pamela Cundell. Abigail Thaw. Gerald Moon. Matthew Radford. Frank Harling. Ken Farrington. Jaqueline Morgan. Malcolm McFee. Andrew Downie. And to the late Peter Bryant for directing it.

To friends, who not only put up with my obsession, but read my early drafts, and in so many ways enabled me to put this book together. Maurice Stewart. Gerald Moon. Brian Jones. Marian Kamlish. Jennie Bisset. Lucia Stuart. David Harris and Guy Rowston.

Every effort has been made to contact possible owners of copyright.

PROLOGUE

It was early evening. With only nine days to wait for the Christmas of 1897, there was a festive spirit in the capital. Shop and office workers, collecting coats and hats, spilled out, eager to join the crowds in the gas lit streets. The pavements were packed. People jostled good humouredly amid newsboys, shoe blacks and sellers of seasonal trimmings. Traders shouted their wares above a jangle of street music and the clatter of hooves. In the gutters, sandwich-board men advertised the Pantomime as they tried to avoid jeers and kicks from passing omnibus conductors. Beggars held out grimy hands, buttonhole sellers looked for likely customers, and painted prostitutes began their stroll down towards the theatres.

The air smelled of fog, horses and roasting chestnuts, with the occasional sharp tang from the oyster-seller's barrow. Crowds were already streaming over Waterloo Bridge towards the Gaiety Theatre, where six new electric lamps now lit up the ever popular Strand. Late Victorian Londoners liked going out. For many there was little home comfort and the streets were endlessly fascinating. Many flocked to the Music Hall, of which there were eight near Leicester Square and over three hundred spread over the great city. For those who could afford it, one of the favourite pre Christmas treats was a visit to the theatre and, at the end of this century, one of the largest and most popular was the Adelphi.

The first theatre on the Adelphi site was built by one John

1

Scott who had made a fortune selling washing blue. An adoring parent, when his daughter wished to show off her histrionic talent, he bought the adjoining shops to his own in the Strand. He then pulled them all down and simply built her a theatre of her own, calling it, with supreme confidence, the 'SANS PAREIL'. Miss Scott's 'Entertainment' was a success and the opening night in November 1806 finished with fireworks.

Now, almost a century later, completely rebuilt and renamed, the Adelphi was managed by the Gatti brothers, Agostino and Stephano. This Italian- Swiss family had made a good living with a restaurant and a Music Hall, under the arches near Hungerford Bridge. However, when the site was needed for the building of Charing Cross Station, the Gattis had been sufficiently compensated to expand. They now ran a very popular restaurant, with entrances in both the Strand and Adelaide Street, as well as several Music Halls, and, most importantly, for the last twenty years they had also held the licence of the Adelphi theatre.

The Adelphi was firmly established as the home of the ever popular melodrama and this continuity of good management had enabled a semi permanent company of actors, writers, set designers and craftsmen to ensure that their loyal public got what they wanted. Audiences flocked to the Adelphi to be thrilled as much by the spectacle as by the broad acting of their favourites. Shipwrecks, snowstorms, battles, mountain rescues, the French Foreign Legion; all were depicted to great effect. The heroes, no matter in what peril they might find themselves, were valiant; the heroines were rescued in the nick of time, and the villains, however dastardly, always got their come-uppance. The Adelphi could be relied upon for a thrilling night out.

The Strand was crowded. Those on foot stopped to watch their betters descend from carriages, and sighed at the fashions which they would never be able to afford. The evening was chilly. There was much clutching of sable, and silver fox across slender throats. There was the occasional glimpse of a daringly

2

low cut neckline seductively half-masked by a corsage of flowers and ribbons. Elegant young ladies carried muffs, or fans, and some wore glittering decorations, or feathers, in their upswept hair. It had rained earlier in the day and there were still a few puddles gleaming in the lamplight.

The throngs were happy and excited. Outside the Adelphi, posters advertised the 150th performance of a melodrama called Secret Service by William Gillette. The author was an American actor who had originally starred in the play, bringing over his own company. It had been a great success and the Gatti brothers, having decided to revive it over the Christmas period, had substituted William Terriss, the most popular of the Adelphi heroes, in the leading role.

'Mr Terriss cleverly shows how the pure love of a woman can regenerate a man… The author is well served by the actor.
'How sweet and commendable is the Edith Varney of Miss Millward. She brings to bear on the part, a delicacy, a charm, and a subtle power that is irresistible… '

So ran the notices, and above them were photographs of the two leading players.

William Terriss was undeniably handsome. Although he had just reached fifty, no one would have suspected it. His hair was thick, his eye bold, and he looked vigorous and confident. Jessie Millward was thirty five, small and dark, with a well-rounded figure. Her face had no classic beauty like that of Terriss, her chin was just a little too determined, but she had large, expressive eyes and a pretty mouth. Distinguished and experienced actors, having been in Irving's company, both at the Lyceum and on two of his American tours, for the last few years they had played opposite each other in one melodrama after another at the Adelphi. They were firm favourites with an adoring public, so much so that when Terriss occasionally appeared without her, his audiences did not approve.

The crowds pressed forward to watch the audience for that night's performance make their way into the brightly lit foyer. The last tickets were sold and the usual boards announcing a full house were put outside. The gallery and the pit filled first. Arriving early to watch others take their seats was part of the fun. Young men and girls leaned forward to gasp and point. They stared at the growing array of dazzling, starched shirt-fronts filing into the boxes and the stalls, and at the wide sweeps of satin or lace, framing the elegant shoulders of their partners. Diamonds glittered, fans were unfolded and programmes scanned. As the few remaining spaces were taken, the last minutes before curtain up were filled with excitement and confident expectation.

Not so backstage. Here the scene was one of horror. A trail of bloodstains led from the private entrance of the Adelphi in Maiden Lane, to the foot of the staircase leading to the dressing rooms. A small group of people stood helplessly around the Adelphi hero, William Terriss, now slumped to the ground. He was half supported in the arms of Jessie Millward, who had caught him as he fell and now knelt beside him. All were in shock.

Mr Budd, the Assistant Manager, clenched his thin hands as if praying. Mr Harry Graves, Terriss's friend who had accompanied him to the theatre that evening, turned his head in disbelief as he fought back the tears. Other members of the company, hearing the disturbance, raced downstairs to stand mute and helpless. A waiter, from Rules Restaurant opposite, ran in with a glass of brandy. All were transfixed by the tableau before them.

Terriss wore a heavy coat over a tweed suit, the front of which was saturated with blood. As Jessie Millward tried to undo his jacket Terriss stirred, his handsome face, pale and contorted with pain.

"Jess, Jess, I am stabbed," he whispered.

"Don't try to talk, Will." Frantically, she turned to the onlookers." Somebody send for a doctor. Oh, dear God ... he's bleeding so."

"The doctor is coming," said Mr Lang the Manager, his mouth trembling, his face the colour of putty.

In the shadows behind him a thin, dark-haired woman began to weep quietly. A Police Inspector with his Constable strode into the passage but then stood, equally helplessly, looking on. All heads turned again as Doctor Hayward and a colleague from Charing Cross Hospital rushed in. There was a stirring of relief and hope as they knelt beside Terriss. Dr Hayward ripped open the bloodstained shirt and under-vest. The two men exchanged a quick glance before his partner, tight-lipped, left swiftly. Doctor Hayward applied ice and pressure pads to the deep, four inch wound but nothing it seemed could staunch the blood. More blood seeped slowly out from underneath Terriss's shoulder.

Jessie looked desperately from one to the other. "You must get him to hospital!"

Doctor Hayward shook his head. "I'm afraid there's no hope."

"What are you saying?"

"His wounds are too deep," said the doctor gently." We cannot move him."

Terriss stirred again. This time his voice was stronger.

"My God! My God! Get away. Get away!" he rasped, his chest heaving.

Doctor Hayward got to his feet and moved back. The petrified onlookers watched as Terriss felt for Jessie Millward's hand. He held it against his cheek.

"Jess, Jess," he whispered. His troubled eyes slowly closed. His breathing stopped.

The group stirred momentarily as the other doctor reappeared at the door, carrying a bag containing resuscitation equipment. One look was sufficient to tell him that it was not needed. No one moved. In a dreadful moment of silent helplessness Jessie screamed.

She rocked the dead man in her arms. "No! No!" she shouted. "You can't die! Will ... my darling, you can't die now ..."

She gave his shoulder a little, impatient shake as if to wake him. Blood oozed out. In the horrified silence she looked up at the ring of frozen faces.

"He can't die now." Her voice was harsh. Looking down at the dead man in her arms, she echoed, as if bewildered. "Oh, not now." She lifted her head again.

"We are going to ... to Australia," she pleaded.

No one spoke. Mr Lang the Manager cleared his throat. "Mr Budd..." he faltered.

Mr Budd, his Assistant, stepped forward as if in a trance. Mr Lang drew him aside.

"God! This is terrible," he muttered. "A disaster ... we must make an announcement, Budd. There's no question ... no question of carrying on with the performance. Yes. I know we've an understudy but - under the circumstances ..."

"Quite, sir," Mr Budd tried hard to collect his wits.

"We can't hold the curtain any longer. I'm needed here. I rely on you to make an announcement, Budd. Use your discretion ...just say there's ... there's been an accident ... and .. of course ... that they can have their money returned."

Mr Budd took a deep breath and hurried off, while the Police Inspector spoke quietly to the two Doctors who were packing up. Then he turned to the Manager. "Mr Lang," he said formally. "I shall of course be taking a statement from everyone but ... the first thing I must have is the name and address of the deceased's next of kin."

"Certainly, Inspector," Mr Lang swallowed. In the small beat of silence which followed, curious eyes were turned on Jessie Millward who still knelt before them cradling the dead man.

"Mr Terriss's wife and family live at The Cottage, No 2

Bedford Park," said Mr Lang in a loud, strained voice, and the small, dark, weeping figure in the shadows behind him stepped forward and, putting her arms around Jessie Millward, helped her to her feet and led her gently away.

In the now restless auditorium, pocket watches were being consulted, as a pale-faced Mr Budd stepped through the curtain and stood blinking in the light. The audience grew quiet. Mr Budd took a deep breath and began nervously.

"Ladies and gentlemen ...

"Speak up!" yelled someone from the gallery. There was a titter, quickly subdued.

"Ladies and gentlemen," Mr Budd began again. "I am deeply grieved and pained to announce.." The hush was immediate. "To announce that our beloved friend Mr Terriss has met with a serious, nay, terrible accident which will render the performance of Secret Service this evening, quite impossible ... "

There was a gasp, and groans, as the audience turned to one another in disbelief.

"I would ask you to pass out into the street as quietly as possible," he continued. "It is hardly necessary for me to tell you that your money will be returned at the pay- boxes."

In the general hubbub of speculation which followed, a much relieved Mr Budd escaped into the wings. As the auditorium cleared and queues formed at the pay-boxes, news of the stabbing had already begun to filter outside. Crowds collected round the official Stage Door in Bull Court, and all along Maiden Lane.

At the front of the theatre, the audience, as they left, were questioned by anxious bystanders. Rumours abounded and the Strand was blocked with enquirers, especially when all the lights outside the Adelphi were extinguished. William Terriss was one of the most popular actors in London both with the public and his profession. As the news sped round the other theatres, shocked fellow actors and stage crews were full of genuine sorrow.

Terriss's body was carried upstairs and laid on a divan in his dressing room. It was here that Seymour Hicks, his son-in-law, who was at that time playing round the corner at the Gaiety Theatre, found him. Seymour Hicks had been ready to go on stage when he heard the dreadful news.

The understudy was put on and he rushed to the Adelphi; while his dresser, Fred, was sent to Bedford Park, where Terriss's son, Tom, had gone home after a rehearsal earlier in the day. The dresser found it impossible to tell what had happened. All he would say was that the young man must come to the theatre.

They were met at the stage door by Harry Nicholls. The leading comic actor in the company, sadly told Tom Terriss of his father's death. But it was not until Tom touched his father's cold face that he understood that it was true. As his legs crumpled, Seymour Hicks steadied him.

He and Seymour comforted each other and then together went to Jessie Millward's dressing room. Jessie sat motionless. Lottie, her maid and companion, looked up with relief as they entered.

"I've tried to get her to take a little brandy, Mr Seymour, but she won't touch it."

"Jessie, my dear," Seymour embraced her, the tears streaming down his face. But it was as if she did not hear him. She gazed at her reflection in the mirror, motionless, except for her hands which twisted and twisted a little handkerchief. Tom, his grief overcoming him again, left the room and Seymour soon followed him.

Mrs Pateman, one of the oldest members of the company, came to her next. "You must let yourself cry, Jessie, my dear, " she begged. "You mustn't bottle it all up like this."

But there were no tears. Jessie Millward sat small and still, like a little bird on a cold day. The other actors left the theatre in ones and twos. Shocked and sad, they hardly knew what to do with an evening of such unexpected and unwelcome leisure.

Still Jessie did not move and Lottie watched her anxiously. At about half past nine Jessie turned slowly from the mirror. Lottie held out her mistress's cloak of dark blue velvet with a sable collar and Jessie allowed herself to be wrapped in the soft, warm fabric.

"There's a good girl," said Lottie. "Shall I call a cab, Miss Jessie?" she asked gently, as she fastened the cloak at the neck, looking intently at her mistress. "No." Jessie spoke at last. "I'll walk."

"Are you sure?" Lottie looked worried. "There'll be lots of people about still. Do let me call a cab."

"No. I need to walk, Lottie. Please! Can't you understand?" Jessie's voice wavered.

"Of course. We'll walk together." Lottie put on her own cloak and picked up Jessie's dressing case. She took her arm and they left the dressing room, switching off the light. The small group of people still outside the Stage Door fell silent as Jessie emerged. They stood back respectfully to let her pass. She looked straight ahead and the watching faces were full of pity. As the two women walked up Regent Street towards Jessie's flat near Hanover Square, news-boys ran by shouting.

"Murder of William Terriss! Murder of William Terriss!" their young voices charged with the thrill of it all. Lottie shuddered but Jessie made no sign.

Later that night William Terriss's body was taken to the mortuary while Jessie Millward sat up until the next day dawned. Two people who had so loved each other and worked together for fifteen years had been ripped apart. William Terriss, so vibrant and generous a person, cruelly murdered, and Jessie's life forever saddened.

But there was yet another cruelty for Jessie to endure. In the elaborate mourning process which followed, Jessie Millward, as far as Victorian society was concerned, had no place. William Terriss's reputation was to be protected at all costs. If this meant ignoring the woman he had loved so faithfully so be it.

Will Terriss, and little Jessie Millward. Two Victorian actors – immensely popular then – almost forgotten today; though, at the time, Terriss's murder was as much a sensation as that of John Lennon. What were they really like, these two Victorian lovers? How did they meet? Why was he murdered?

This is a story of love, jealousy, madness and hypocrisy.

CHAPTER ONE

MAY 22 1861 WINDERMERE COLLEGE
WESTMORLAND

My dear Bob,
'We have begun cricket and I am in the fifth eleven. I have a good lot of marbles, and I have got a nice little flask. I don't think I told you that I had a fight with Fairie, a new fellow, about as big as Rushton, and Jip Gibson was my second; and I think I fought very well '...

Mary Lewin sighed before handing the letter back to Bob, her middle son. "Why must he get into so many fights?" she asked wearily. "I don't know what your poor Father would have thought about it all. He was such a gentle person."

Bob Lewin folded the letter and smiled as he put it in his pocket.

" Will's all right, Mother. He's just a bit headstrong – and he does usually win you know. At least his spelling has improved."

He put his arm around his Mother's shoulders." You mustn't worry so."

"How can I not worry?" Mary Lewin fretted. "This is, after all, the third school. When is he going to settle down? I declare he's more trouble than the rest of you put together."

William Terriss, or William Lewin as he was then, the youngest of five children, was born on February 20 1847 at 7, Circus Road, St John's Wood. The family was affluent and well connected. His Grandfather had been private secretary to Warren Hastings in Calcutta and another relative was George Grote, an eminent historian. The family lived for a time in both Lewisham and Clapham before moving back across the river to Bayswater.

His Father, George Herbert Lewin, was a Barrister with chambers in Pall Mall but ill health prevented him from practising as often as he would have wished. He died when William was ten years old and the boy was removed from the Blue Coat School in Sussex, where he had been a somewhat reluctant pupil.

His next school was in Littlehampton, also in Sussex, but his stay was, once again, short lived. Windermere College in Westmorland had been chosen because it was run by a relative of the Lewins. Both his brother Bob and his two cousins had all been satisfactory pupils. Young William was proving much more of a problem.

He was an extremely handsome, cheerful boy, with thick hair, straight eyebrows over bright blue eyes that looked at you without wavering, a strong, well-shaped nose and a full, mischievous mouth. He had inexhaustible energy and was a good athlete. Although popular with both teachers and pupils, he was forever getting into scrapes. Rules were irksome things not to be taken too seriously and, within a year, another escapade brought his stay at Windermere College to an end. Returning to London he was next enrolled at Bruce Castle School in Tottenham. One might have hoped that a school that boasted a sixteenth century round tower with a resident ghost might have appealed to young William but, after yet more unruly behaviour, he ran away.

Although such a trial to his Mother, he was insouciant to a degree and when, after a family conference, a career in the

Merchant Navy was suggested, he happily agreed. He was delighted when a berth was obtained for him with Messrs Green and Co, and even more delighted with the uniform, which he donned at once.

In the weeks before he was due to leave, he enjoyed himself enormously swaggering around the streets of Bayswater. The day came for him to set sail. The whole family went down to Gravesend to see him off. His sisters cried as they waved him goodbye, but Mrs Lewin felt only relief that, at last, her whirlwind of a son would be both challenged and disciplined.

Within two weeks her hopes were dashed by a telegram from William who had slipped ashore at Plymouth. He had, he said, already found that a seafaring life was much more boring than he had expected, he couldn't possibly stay and he was on his way home.

The family once again conferred about his future. Mrs Lewin's eldest son, Thomas, had had a successful army career in India and was now Deputy Commissioner in Chittagong. The Lewins felt that perhaps the further away William went the better, and William – ever eager to try something new – was sent to Assam where his brother obtained him a position with a firm of tea planters. Predictably this did not engage him for very long and after coming home again via Calcutta, he entertained his sisters for hours with accounts of shipwrecks and days spent under burning suns. The skills of an actor were unwittingly being honed. At this time he was left a small legacy by an uncle and for a short time proceeded to lead the life of a rich young man about town until the money had all disappeared.

* * *

A few months later his godfather, John Henry Graves, announced his intention of accompanying a wealthy friend on a short Mediterranean cruise.

"I was wondering if we might take young Will with us," he asked Mrs Lewin one evening.

"Dear Harry," she replied. "What a simply splendid idea."

An excited William, now eighteen, and determined to look the part, took from his wardrobe his so briefly worn midshipman's uniform. The party were to travel to Weston-super-Mare by train to join the yacht and, money being no problem, a special carriage was hired for the journey and attached to the night mail from Paddington. William was thrilled by the whole affair and soon began to realise that for some reason he seemed to be creating quite a stir at the station. He wasn't sure who they thought he was but clearly it was someone of importance, and William instinctively played along.

It was such a convincing performance that by the time the train arrived at Weston-super-Mare the staff of the station and the Royal Bath Hotel, where they were to stay overnight ,were all quite sure that Queen Victoria's second son, His Royal Highness, Prince Alfred, who was in the navy at the time, was honouring them with his presence.

In vain did Harry Graves try to tell the hotel staff, and the growing crowd of visiting dignitaries who arrived the next morning, that it was all a mistake. By the time breakfast was finished a large crowd had collected and the bells of Weston-super-Mare were ringing. When they ordered a carriage to take them on their way, the most resplendent in all the town, complete with two postillions, was put at their disposal and an embarrassed Mr Graves and his friend were mobbed and fêted while a delighted William bowed, waved and smiled as to the manner born.

"William!" thundered his godfather. "Will you behave!"

But William would not. Could not. The joke was too good. No Royal Prince could have been more charming or more splendid in his uniform. He leaned from the carriage to accept small tokens of local esteem, ranging from bouquets of flowers to small phials of perfume, with a perfect ease that would have graced an actual son of the Sovereign. His own Mother had a few weeks without worries, the cruise was a great success and he returned home bronzed and eager to try something new.

He excelled at all kinds of sport, and as his brother Bob was now a houseman at St Mary's Hospital Paddington, William played half-back in the hospital rugby team. He was immensely popular with the students and even briefly flirted with the idea of a medical career. He would use his adoring sisters as guinea pigs, bandaging them and prescribing medicines until his brother Bob anxiously dissuaded him from all thoughts of a medical career.

"You're far too reckless, old chap," he insisted. "Come on, Will, admit it."

William looked up from the pages of an atlas that he was turning. "You're probably right, Bob. Something else is bound to turn up."

One of the students at St Mary's had a brother apprenticed at that time to a firm of engineers. "I say, George," enquired William one day after a strenuous game. "How does your brother like engineering?'

"He likes it very well. Says it suits him admirably."

William thought for a moment. "Well ... who knows. I could give it a try. It might just suit me too."

He was duly apprenticed to the same firm and, once again, it seems to have been the uniform that most appealed to him. He amused all his friends by strolling about in dirty overalls with his face and hands daubed with grease. But the actual business of engineering quickly palled.

By now his brother had qualified as a Doctor and William delighted in embarrassing him. Bob, who adored his younger brother, never quite knew what he would do next. On one occasion they were travelling together by train up to Charing Cross. Bob, sitting opposite William in a crowded carriage, saw him wink and waited in dread for what might follow, but William closed his eyes and seemed to sleep. Bob relaxed until, to his horror, William began to twitch.

As the twitch became a convulsion Bob looked determinedly out of the window until he was nudged by his neighbour. "I say," said the man anxiously. Your mate's taken bad."

Bob took his brother's hand. "Stop it, Will," he said. William rolled his eyes and the 'epileptic fit' grew worse.

"He needs a Doctor, if you ask me," shouted a woman in the corner. The rest of the carriage agreed.

"I AM a Doctor!" exclaimed the wretched Bob, as he was forced to help William descend at the next station in order to take him to hospital. As the train pulled away, the woman shouted "You unfeeling brute!"

William collapsed onto the platform with laughter.

* * *

Some of his rugby playing friends suggested that they should all join the St Mary's Hospital Dramatic Society. They soon began to put on plays and sketches to raise money to augment the hospital funds. Young Will Lewin, just twenty and still hopelessly undecided about his future, was entrusted with three lines in a production of *Bombastes Furioso,* a popular farce written by one William Barnes Rhodes and first performed at the Haymarket Theatre in 1810. His family having no connection whatsoever with the stage, this was his first encounter with theatricals.

By a curious coincidence, in a house not so far away from Paddington, where the stage was almost the only topic of conversation, a little girl was making her debut in the very same play. In a drawing room production of *Bombastes Furioso* in which many famous men of the theatre were taking part for the fun of it, Jessie Millward had no lines at all, but was to play the drummer. Unfortunately the excitement of it was too much, she had a tantrum and was carried screaming from the room. She was just five years old.

William Lewin began to enjoy acting and, with his charm and good looks, was soon in demand by many amateur companies in London, but it was in Birmingham where he was staying with a friend that he got his first chance to work professionally. He went to see a production of *Arrah-na-Pogue*, a play by Dion Boucicault, in which the hero, Sean, had to climb an ivy-covered tower to rescue the heroine. The actor playing the part, one James Rogers, although vastly experienced was also equally vast in size. The tower was slowly lowered, as he climbed, to create an impression of scaling a great height but, each succeeding night, the climb became ever more difficult. Furthermore, on his arrival at the top the hero had to fight the villain and throw him over the battlements. At this point a breathless Rogers could hardly stand.

He met the young Will Lewin. On learning that he wished to go on the stage, he offered him a guinea a night if he would, in an identical costume, do the climb for him, while he calmly waited already hidden at the top. It was just the sort of lark that appealed to Will and, he thought, a jolly easy way to earn a guinea. Rogers gallantly allowed him to take a call at the end which he did with such style that he soon had a small following in Birmingham.

The next year he obtained a small part at the Prince of Wales Theatre in Birmingham in another play by Boucicault called 'The Flying Scud'. Unfortunately on the first night he dried. After beginning the speech, "*Lady Woodby has come to town…*"he was unable to remember any more. He paused, frowned, then shrugged and, smiling his devastating smile, said graciously, "And the rest!" and walked off. He was called 'And The Rest' teasingly by his friends for weeks afterwards.

But acting was a new challenge and he determined to come back to London and try his luck. Not wishing to bring disgrace on the family – the theatre not being even remotely considered as a suitable profession for a gentleman – he changed his name to William Terriss.

CHAPTER TWO

Jessie Millward's family were quite different. Charlie Millward, Jessie's Father, first came to London for a few days in 1851. He had supposed he might visit the Great Exhibition. He could hardly go back to Liverpool and admit that he hadn't. But much more important to Charlie Millward was a piece, *The Follies of the Day*, which he had co-written and which was opening at the Adelphi Theatre in the Strand. As he travelled, he thought of all his early struggles from shipping clerk to journalist with but one ambition, to work in the theatre in some way or other. From his youth he had been involved with amateur theatricals and had often been both writer, producer and performer. He smiled to remember those early concerts in the coffee houses of Liverpool, subsidised by local philanthropists like one, Mr George Melly. Audiences could get coffee for a penny, while draughts, newspapers and, most importantly for the newly formed Liverpool Literary and Dramatic Society, entertainments, were free.

Charlie Millward was 'Big in Liverpool', but further afield he had not, so far, been successful. A very early piece he had written entitled *The Rose, Shamrock and Thistle* or *Gleanings from the Minstrelsy of England, Scotland and Ireland* had proved, when taken on tour to the Isle of Man, to have a title longer than its run.

So meagre were the takings that on the second night the

piano had to go, and on the third, the gas was cut off. But now, to succeed at the Adelphi, to hear his words spoken by established actors would realise his dreams. He was a handsome, popular man and had already many literary friends in London. They gathered to support him. *Follies of the Day* was a success and ran for seventy one nights.

Charlie Millward soon left Liverpool for London, married and began a family. After a son was born, he named his eldest daughter, Jessie, and she was eventually followed by five other children. Always convivial, he was one of the earliest members of the Savage Club who used to meet in a pot house off Drury Lane. The only qualification for joining was to be a 'working man in Literature or Art'. The members sought a suitable name for their club and, the 'Addison', and the 'Goldsmith' having been rejected, and moving as they did from tavern to tavern for their early meetings, they eventually decided on the 'Savage' in memory of Richard Savage, a drunken and somewhat disreputable poet. Doctor Johnson had considered his work full of 'moments of splendour', but Savage was unable to sustain his creative endeavour and he died in a debtor's prison in 1743. His melancholy end does not seem to have deterred the many eminent men who have, to this day, become 'Savages'.

A custom grew to hold monthly hot-pot dinners for some of the members in each other's houses, and nowhere were they more welcome than at the Millward's home in Malden Crescent, North London, where on these occasions the children would be put to bed especially early. But Jessie Millward would be far from sleep. She was nine years old and in the next bed her sister Lil slept soundly, one arm clasping a wooden doll with a painted face and wide open eyes that saw nothing.

Jessie her great, dark eyes staring at the ceiling, imagined she saw in the uneven swirls in the plaster, clouds and landscapes and a floating dragon. If she turned her head, the dragon became a mermaid. She sighed, for, from far away downstairs in the drawing room came the sound of voices and laughter. That was where she always wanted to be. She knew that all her Father's friends would be sitting round the table that had been pulled out to its full length with extra sections added. All that day and the day before, her Mother, and the girl who helped out on these occasions, had been busy preparing food. Jessie had been allowed to shine the spoons and the candlesticks with a yellow duster, and even help arrange them on the table.

When it was the Millward's turn to give the Sunday hot-pot supper for the Savages and their friends she would creep out of bed and hang over the bannisters to watch the arrivals. Many of them were familiar, Squire Bancroft and his wife Marie, actor-managers, Mr Tom Robertson the playwright. The young actors Mr John Hare, Mr Henry Irving and her special favourite, Mr Johnny Toole. Others she did not know but they were all connected with writing or the theatre and they often arrived with their pockets, like her Father's, stuffed with scripts. How she longed to be old enough to stay up. One day, she said to herself, she would be a really famous actress and stay up all night if she felt like it.

When she was ten, Jessie was sent to the North London Collegiate School started in 1850 by the formidable Miss Buss. By now the school had grown to over seven hundred pupils and Jessie was at first overwhelmed by the sheer size of the place and the unaccustomed routine.

"I'll never fit in, Mama," she wailed. "You can't speak on the stairs and you're not even allowed to hurry … and you mustn't get your skirt wet even if it's raining and … and I lost my gloves yesterday and now my name is in the 'Appearing Book'. It's truly dreadful!"

Her Mother was sympathetic but had two younger children and a new baby to concern her.

"It's high time you settled down,' she told Jessie. "You will soon get accustomed to it. You are an intelligent girl and we don't want that dismal face in this house, thank you."

Jessie began to make friends and soon her naturally high spirits returned. The curriculum was varied for Miss Buss was passionate about the need for girls to get a good education. This included 'Natural Science – with elements of experimentation, Calisthenics and Political and Domestic economy' as well as French, German and Latin. Drama, much to Jessie's disappointment, mostly consisted of 'Tableaux Vivants' taken from original paintings by the father of the Headmistress. Scripture, Liturgy and Christian Evidences, were taught by the Reverend Septimus Buss, her brother. He combined his scholastic duties with the care of the parish of Wapping, and the Chaplaincy of St. Pancras Workhouse.

Miss Buss, highly respected as a forward looking educationist, was austere, plump and exceedingly dignified. She had small, keen eyes and a long upper lip which gave her a solemn look. She was not in the least amused when she caught her new pupil doing a wickedly accurate impression of herself.

Jessie began to enjoy school and she was enthralled with her first experience of the annual distribution of prizes. The nearby Exeter Hall was hired, the pupils dressed in white, and as the organ thundered the national anthem, Princess Mary, Duchess of Teck, arrived to present the awards. Gradually Jessie's early talent was recognised and, at the monthly Dorcas meetings when the girls sewed to improve their souls, and make clothes for poor children, she was usually chosen to read aloud to the industrious young needlewomen. Here she was in her element and often reduced them, and herself, to floods of tears with a particularly sad passage.

Her Father still kept up his Liverpool connections by starting a weekly paper called ' *The Porcupine*' for which he wrote a London Letter. Jessie was enlisted to help him. The political comments she found less interesting, but the theatrical notices were a different matter, as she knew so many of the people involved. The school years passed. Although Jessie did not always appreciate the discipline she, like all Miss Buss's girls, was taught to question, to value herself as a woman, and to have a concern for others less fortunate. And whenever school life became too rigid, she cheered herself with her continuing secret ambition to become an actress.

She was now allowed to stay up for a while when the Millwards entertained, and by far her greatest thrill was to hear Henry Irving recite. The recent success at the Lyceum of his *Hamlet*, followed by *Macbeth*, were making him an increasingly popular and charismatic leading actor. His voice mesmerised her with its great range of expression, and she would finally go up to bed with her heart thumping with excitement.

One evening Irving persuaded her Father to allow Jessie to perform. She began nervously but then, as always, lost herself in the piece. Irving, sitting a little apart, watched her, his chin on his hands. When the applause had died away he turned to Mrs Millward.

"Of course, your daughter will go on the stage," he said softly.

Jessie's heart leapt but her Mother answered.

"Certainly not, Henry. I would rather see her in her grave."

Jessie prayed that she didn't really mean it but her Mother would not discuss it.

Her Father had a Pantomime running at the Adelphi when a man who owed him money died, leaving him, as part of the debt, a Monumental Mason's business in Abney Park, not far from the cemetery of the same name. Somewhat to everyone's surprise it proved to be of sound financial benefit and his fellow Savages dubbed him with new billing.

"Charlie Millward – From Grave to Gay"

Many quite well known stars of the pantomime would bring songs to the house for Charlie Millward to write special lyrics and Jessie would be called upon to play them through. She began to accompany her Father to the theatre where she hero-worshipped the performers. One evening he announced his intention of taking her to the Adelphi to see *Romeo and Juliet*. Her Mother, unsure about its suitability, was nevertheless eventually persuaded to allow her to go. Motionless the whole way through, when the curtain fell, Jessie lay back in her seat and sobbed uncontrollably.

To cheer her up, her Father took her backstage to meet the real, and still very much alive, Juliet, played by Adelaide Neilson. Jessie was still so stunned both by the performance and by the beauty of the actress in her embroidered silk dressing gown that she was quite unable to speak. Adelaide Neilson took her hand. The dark, tear-smudged eyes and solemn little face moved her, and she suddenly unclasped the cross of opals which she wore around her neck and gave them to the astonished girl. As she fastened them she said "May this be the heaviest cross you ever have to bear, my child.'

CHAPTER THREE

William Terriss, meanwhile, had returned to London. With his usual straightforward approach to life, and having decided to try a theatrical career, he determined to call on one of the leading managers of the day. The fact that he had no appointment did not deter him. He simply persisted.

As Squire Bancroft walked up to his front door it flew open and his maid, clearly agitated, ran out to meet him.

"What on earth is the matter, Maggie?"

"Oh, Sir ..." Maggie cried breathlessly."It's that young man I told you about. The one who keeps calling. He came again and when I said you were out he ... he just smiled and said he would wait this time and ... I'm afraid ..." Maggie bit her lip, "he's in the drawing room."

"Is he indeed!" Squire Bancroft's face reddened. "We'll soon see about that!"

"I'm so sorry, Sir." Maggie took his hat and cane and followed him nervously inside. Her master stopped briefly before the mirror to smooth his hair, then turned and smiled at her. "You're not to worry, girl, it wasn't your fault." He rubbed his hands. "And, in a moment, Maggie, you can have the pleasure of seeing this young intruder out."

Squire Bancroft marched into his drawing room where a very handsome young man standing by the window, strode forward, hand outstretched.

"I know this is an unforgivable intrusion, Sir," he said quickly, "but I could see no other way of getting to meet you."

"Well really, I have to say, Sir, this is hardly the most … " began Squire Bancroft in his most intimidating voice. It had no effect.

"Oh, but please, Sir," the visitor insisted," I shall not detain you long. My name is William Terriss and I have just returned from playing at the Prince of Wales – oh, not your Prince of Wales, Sir – although I have high hopes so to do ..."

"Have you indeed!" Bancroft's stare met an equally determined look from two bright blue eyes under very straight brows.

"Yes, Sir. I have just returned from Birmingham where I think I may say I had some success."

Here the young man smiled so disarmingly that Squire Bancroft's anger began to fade. There was something totally fascinating about this young ... what did he say his name was? ... Terriss?

The young man appeared quite at home. He moved back to the window, pulled aside the curtain and looked out. "I was born in that house across the road," he said. "But when my father died we moved. I was ten."

For a moment he paused as though lost in thought, then turned and smiled again, squaring his broad shoulders. "I am determined to make a career in the theatre,Sir," he said, "and I am resolved that you should give me an engagement. I'll not let you down, Sir. You have my word."

Squire Bancroft, 'Squire' being his Christian name, not his title, and his wife Marie, were among London's leading actor-managers. They had had great success with comedies written by Tom Robertson, and at that time ran the 'Prince of Wales' a small theatre off the Tottenham Court Road. Some years later they would take over the management of the Haymarket Theatre and before the century was out Squire Bancroft would be knighted for his services to the theatrical profession.

William Terriss's bravado paid off and he was given the small part of Lord Cloudwrays in Bancroft's next production. The role was hardly more than an elegant walk on but all his friends came to support him, cheering his every appearance and, no doubt, enraging his fellow actors. His brother Bob, however, was not impressed. As they walked home together after the first performance Terriss, well pleased with himself, waited for at least a grudging word of praise. "Well, Bob, what did you think?" he burst out.

Bob seemed embarrassed. "Chuck it up, dear boy," he said at last." You'll never do." It seemed as though he might have been right for at the end of the run Terriss was not re-engaged.

With so little actual experience in London the only job on offer was to play a brigand in an *Equestrian Epic* at Astley's theatre in Lambeth. William was content however, for he enjoyed the riding and still had energy to spare, joining a swimming club in Marylebone where he won a silver cup. He also got married.

It was at Margate where he was sporting in the sea with friends and outshining them all, for swimming was a passion with Terriss, that a certain young actress, Isabel Lewis, first set approving eyes on him. She had remarkably small hands and feet, clear, grey eyes and a deliciously neat, turned up nose. Terriss made sure he was introduced and, with his usual aplomb, suggested not only lunch but a drive. The young lady, protesting that she had to catch the three o'clock train back to London, Terriss turned his watch back two hours and assured her that she had plenty of time. When they eventually reached the station where it was now the five-thirty train which waited he looked into her eyes and convinced her that his watch had stopped.

In a few weeks he had also convinced her that she should marry him. He knew that his family would not approve and so Brother Bob and his godfather, Henry Graves, were the only ones invited to the quiet wedding and the happy couple left for their honeymoon in Richmond on a bus. Isabel gave up her short career and began life with her young, impetuous husband. He was twenty three and she just twenty two.

Coming back each night from Astley's he would make her laugh with stories of his exploits. In one scene the horse he rode, called Teddy, was trained to exit by himself on a spoken cue of *"Get thee to the mountains"*. Sadly, one afternoon after the performance the horse dropped dead. The only available substitute for that evening's show was from the nearby stables of the Omnibus Company. They got the horse into the theatre but, in spite of much rehearsing, Teddy's replacement was not very promising. At the performance that night the problem was how to get him to trot offstage on cue.

"We tried everything, Izzie," exclaimed Terriss. "Joe stood in the wings with a great bunch of carrots. I shouted *"Get thee to the mountains,"* as loudly as I could. Nothing. We couldn't play the rest of the piece with the horse on stage could we? And I could hardly ride him off and then walk back on again. So I tried again and slapped his rump. 'GET THEE TO THE MOUNTAINS!' I yelled. He flicked his tail but wouldn't budge. By now we were getting a few snickers from the crowd."

"I'm not surprised," Isabel giggled. "What on earth did you do?"

"I suddenly remembered," said William. "He was, after all, a bus horse. I stamped three times on the floor as hard as I could – like the conductors do – and shouted *'Right ahead!'* and he trotted off like a lamb."

When this engagement came to an end, with nothing else in view and a young wife to support, Terriss decided that he must try yet another career. He had obtained an introduction to two brothers named Packe who were intent on farming sheep in the Falkland Islands. To the intrepid Terriss the challenge presented by this enormous distance was irresistible; Isabel had little choice. She was reassured by her husband that it would be a capital adventure and that they would undoubtedly make their fortune. Neither of them had any notion of the hardships they were to encounter.

The first part of their journey was to South America on a Brazilian mail packet, the *Douro*, and took six long weeks. Isabel was by now in the early stages of pregnancy which cannot have helped. Their relief on at last reaching Montevideo was short-lived for they found the city not only in the middle of a revolution but also suffering a serious outbreak of yellow fever. Prices of everything were sky high and for nine days they were obliged to stay barricaded in their hotel while fighting raged around them. Finally they obtained a boat to take them onward.

The *Foam* was a small schooner and almost at once they ran into atrocious weather – not uncommon in the South Atlantic. With everything battened down they rode the mountainous seas for days on end. Terriss, undaunted, cheered his wife, turned his hand to anything and encouraged everyone, until, after eighteen days for a journey that normally took a week, at long last the winds calmed sufficiently to allow them to reach Stanley Harbour.

By now, Isabel's pregnancy meant that she had to stay in the comparatively civilised Port Stanley on West Falkland, while the sheep farm turned out to be on the other, Eastern, island, at that time completely undeveloped. The bright dream of becoming an affluent sheep farmer faded and Terriss had to turn his hand to whatever he could. When their daughter Ellaline was born in Stanley's only hotel – The Ship – the little family were forced to think about returning, although in their five months stay they had become hugely popular, the Governor being godfather to the baby.

Large vessels called in very infrequently to the Falklands and Terriss was, as usual, impatient to set off so they took passage on a whaler coming from Honolulu via Cape Horn. The Governor took them out to the boat in his yacht and even provided a live goat to give the child a supply of fresh milk on board. But once again their journey was not to be a smooth one.

The Captain, a Swede of uncertain temper, was so unpopular with the crew that in a mutinous mood they turned to Terriss for support. This did not endear the little family to the Swede who made the voyage as uncomfortable as he could. By the time they landed eventually at Falmouth one would imagine that Isabel had had enough of wandering the world to last her for the rest of her life.

Terriss rented a small cottage in Barnes, settled his little family in and once again went to look for work. This time the theatre proved more accessible and he soon obtained an engagement at Drury Lane where Adelaide Neilson was the new star. He was brilliantly type cast as Robin Hood in an adaptation of *Ivanhoe* and was, this time, retained for the whole season. He succeeded in other roles and had his first taste of Shakespeare when Adelaide Neilson chose *As You Like It* in which he played Silvius.

Unfortunately, in the summer months Drury Lane Theatre became an Opera house, and once again William Terriss found himself out of work. This inactivity was intolerable and one day he met an old school friend who was one of the Tattersalls, a famous horse breeding family. He learned with mounting interest that one of the cousins, Percy, whom he knew slightly, was running a horse agency at Lexington in Kentucky.

"It would be just the thing for you, Will," urged his friend. "And there's money to be made. Why don't you give it a try over the summer?"

It says much for his powers of persuasion and Isabel's devotion that within a week everything, including the baby – not yet a year old – was packed ready to cross the Atlantic once again. The cottage in Barnes was locked and the key left with a neighbour.

The crossing was uneventful but, on arrival, their accommodation in Lexington, Kentucky turned out to be very primitive. Although Terriss was up at five every morning to work with the horses, he found the business was badly organised, profits were not forthcoming and his capital began to dwindle alarmingly. Isabel, doing her best not to pine for her homely cottage in Barnes, found that she was pregnant again.

Terriss, however, had made good friends. He had joined a Masonic lodge whose worshipful master was a wealthy coachbuilder. Learning of Terriss's financial difficulties he generously offered to lend the little family their return fare. Although they travelled steerage, Terriss soon became very popular on board and often brought back to their cabin tit-bits from the captain's table.

Within twenty four hours of landing he had remitted the loan and by the autumn Isabel was settled in the cottage in Barnes, Terriss was back at Drury Lane for the new season, earning money, and a little brother for Ellaline had arrived and was christened Tom. Terriss took his new responsibilities more seriously. Further adventures, no matter how promising were, reluctantly, out of the question but he was much encouraged by a notice he received from one of the most important and perceptive theatre critics of the day.

'Fresh and pleasant, active and intelligent, enthusiastic and natural, stood out among the rest, the 'Malcolm Graeme' of Mr W. Terriss, a young actor who has now made a fair start, and will, no doubt, do uncommonly well,' wrote Clement Scott. *'The contrast between the natural and manly declaration of this young actor and the old-fashioned, stilted style of some of his fellows was very striking, and it is really pleasant to find anyone determined to speak as ordinary people speak, on the boards of a theatre where-in strange tones and emphases prevail.'*

He had seen that, although comparatively inexperienced as an actor, Terriss's somewhat madcap past exploits made him superbly convincing in an heroic role. Coming from Clement Scott this was the kind of notice to gladden any actor's heart and also to alert the managements of the day.

Terriss determined to study his craft. Acting, he began to realise was more than an amusing way to pay the bills, which were increased by a further addition to his family when a second son, William, was born. Isabel, no doubt contented that her third pregnancy had not entailed Transatlantic upheavals, looked after the children, while her husband, with the same enthusiasm that he always brought to anything that he undertook, trained his body and his voice. He watched other actors. William Terriss had at last, in the theatre, found a different sort of challenge; one to last a lifetime.

At the Strand Theatre he gained valuable experience and the beginnings of public acclaim in a series of comedies in which his impudent charm struck exactly the right note. Next he returned to the Drury Lane Theatre and for several years played one hero after another in melodramas, creating the role of Captain Molyneux in the first production in London in 1875 of Dion Boucicault's *The Shaughraun*.

It was at Drury Lane that he first met the very young actor Norman Forbes who played all the juvenile roles. He was a spindly, sensitive boy and appreciated Terriss's kindness to him. He was also fascinated by Terriss's ability to tell the most convincing lies. One evening they were waiting in the wings together when Terriss's dresser rushed in to tell him that he had just seen a certain young actor pocketing one of the selection of ladies' gold watches that Terriss had been sent on approval.

"That's all right, Sam," Terriss said, immediately. "I told him to choose one."

"Oh, I see, Sir," said the surprised dresser.

"Did you really give it to him, Will?" asked young Norman.

"Yes, old chap," said Terriss. "You see he's just got engaged and I thought it would do for his pretty lass."

The next night Norman Forbes asked the young man if it were true that he was engaged to be married.

"Certainly not," he laughed. "Who told you such a cracker?"

On learning that it was Terriss, the young actor fell silent and the next day the watch was returned.

When the season at Drury Lane Theatre ended, Terriss and young Forbes went to the Court Theatre in Sloane Square. Here Terriss had an outstanding success playing opposite a young actress who, throughout her long and magnificent career, would always remain fond of him. Ellen Terry and William Terriss, both then aged thirty one, were perfectly cast opposite one another in a clever dramatisation of *The Vicar of Wakefield* called *Olivia*; Norman Forbes playing Moses, Ellen Terry the title role and Terriss playing against his usual casting as the unprincipled – but devastatingly attractive – young Squire Thornhill. Small wonder that the fair Olivia found him irresistible.

As people they were both fun loving and unconventional, and as actors their two performances became the toast of the town. There were picture postcards of Ellen in her Olivia cap and of Will Terriss complete with blond curls and an eye patch. Ellen Terry's two children, Teddy and Edy, often walked on in the play and they both adored Will Terriss. Often after the performance Terriss would take the Underground from Sloane Square to Charing Cross. One evening Norman Forbes was with him when, hearing the train approaching, Terriss ran down the steep stairs to the platform. But the six foot gate at the bottom slammed shut as the train came in. This device to prevent latecomers did not deter Terriss who vaulted over the gate, climbed onto the train and waved to Norman and a very irate porter.

Apart from the beginning of lifelong friendships, the production was to prove lucky for them all. Henry Irving had just taken over the management of the Lyceum. Refurbishing the theatre both backstage and in the auditorium was to cost him an overdraft of almost £10,000. He was looking for a strong team of actors and immediately recognised in Ellen Terry the leading lady he had dreamed of. Irving with Ellen Terry put the Lyceum back on the theatrical map and on the first night of Irving's *Hamlet* under his own banner the curtain fell to a riot of applause.

Terriss was to wait two years before joining the Lyceum Company and by this time he had become even more popular with the public. His Romeo opposite Adelaide Neilson at the Haymarket, although Shakespeare was never his forte, was so utterly convincing that ladies in the audience were near to swooning. What made him equally attractive to men was that all this adulation did not change him. He was still the open, warm and uncomplicated friend they had always known.

In 1880 the important call to the Lyceum arrived. Irving engaged him to play in *The Corsican Brothers*. The play, already popular with the public, and now with Irving and Terriss in the cast, was an immediate 'sell-out', and notices to that effect were printed in the newspaper. The play was an adaptation of a novel by Alexander Dumas which was itself based on a true story of the telepathic link between identical twins. The twins, in reality English, were transformed into Corsicans – no doubt to make them more exotic – and Irving played the dual role of Louis and Fabien Franchi. Terriss was to play the elegant villain M. De Chateau Renaud.

Irving's company at the Lyceum were extremely deferential to the Guv'nor, as they called him. Strict, even autocratic, he could be scathing to anyone who in his eyes was not serious about his work. He also ensured that his was always the most predominant figure on stage. In the final scene of *The Corsican Brothers* a duel is fought in a snow-covered forest between the twin avenging his brother's death, and the villain. It takes place at night.

At one of the final rehearsals they used the 'snow' for the

first time. The stage crew, poised in the darkened wings, waited as their rubber- wheeled baggage trolleys were loaded with wide- mouthed sacks, filled with tons of salt. On cue, in they ran, silently, tipped up the sacks and quickly spread the salt with large wooden shovels. Irving timed the change, nodded, and in the now, snow-laden, forest clearing the rehearsal continued. Suddenly, Terriss stopped the fighting and called breezily to the limelight man who, as was the custom, was focussed solely on Irving.

"I say, old chap," he asked pleasantly, "Do you think I might have a glimmer of light, too?" The watching actors and stage crew froze.

There was a tomb-like silence. Everyone looked at Irving. Terriss smiled.

"Just to make it easier for us both ... with these swords, you know ... bit dangerous, what?."

The Stage Manager held his breath. Irving put down his sword, paused as if deep in thought, looked across at Terriss who waited calmly and then drawled

"By all means ... let Mr Terriss have a little ... moonlight ..." He then deliberately kicked up some of the snow..." and," he continued, "do let him have a little snow as well!"

The company breathed again and the rehearsal continued.

Irving liked Will Terriss. He found his spontaneous impudence a refreshing change from the sycophancy he usually encountered. He was a good friend. Irving was also a good friend to Charlie Millward and his family and this friendship was to prove important both to Terriss and to Jessie Millward. For it was under his management at the Lyceum that they would, eventually, have their first meeting.

CHAPTER FOUR

"Here we go round the mulberry bush, here we go round the mulberry bush," sang Jessie Millward triumphantly. "And I never have to go to school, ever, ever again! Wheeeeeee!"

"Jessie, stop. You're hurting my arms!" Lilian Millward cried. "And it's not fair. I've still got to go to school for years and years."

Jessie stopped whirling her sister round and, laughing, pulled her onto the sofa.

"I'm sorry, Lil," she smoothed the girl's long fair hair. "It's just such a relief. You can't imagine."

Lillian Millward looked at her sister. Jessie was so different from her and little Flo. They were fair-haired like their father and had blue eyes. Jessie, dark as a gypsy, resembled their Mother. And today she looked so grown up. She had put on her Sunday dress to celebrate. It was made of tussore silk and had a pattern of small red rosebuds on a pale grey background. Lillian looked with envy at Jessie's small waist and marvelled at her amazing bosom which just seemed to have suddenly arrived.

"Now you can be a dear, Lil, and hear my lines" said Jessie, picking up a script from the table.

"It's the very beginning of the second act that I'm still not sure of."

Jessie had joined the Carlton Dramatic Club. They were a

band of enthusiastic amateurs and Jessie, quick to exploit her professional connections, usually got the leading role. They had already given a performance at the St George's Hall and, with school work now a thing of the past, Jessie felt she was one step nearer to her dream of being a real actress. The family had moved into a larger house nearby in Oakley Square and Jessie had her own room. Life seemed perfect.

The previous day her Father had been busy on a script when he complained of feeling unwell. Today he had seemed much better but when she returned that evening from the rehearsal the Doctor was in the hall. His face was grave and her Mother was crying. Her brother Herbert took her hands.

"Pa's very ill, Jess. He's had a stroke. He can't ..." the young man broke down. "He can't talk ..."

Jessie flew up the stairs, but her brother raced after her and grabbed her arm. "Not now. We mustn't disturb him." Jessie sank down on the stairs and wept.

For days the seven children crept silently about the normally noisy house. The Doctor came every morning but at the end of the week he told them all that, although their Father's life was out of immediate danger, there was little likelihood of him ever making a full recovery.

Fortunately the Stone Mason's business that had originally caused the 'Savages' so much mirth brought in some money, but it was soon clear that the older children would have to find paid employment.

For a young lady in 1880 the obvious, and only respectable, choice was to become a Governess. Jessie, so recently released from school, hated the very idea and she was thrilled and also surprised when her Mother finally agreed that she could try to become an actress.

"I am very reluctant," said her Mother seriously. "However, if you really think that is your vocation I will give my permission ... but you must start under Mrs Kendal."

Jessie knew that Mrs Kendal's reputation as 'the Matron of

British Drama' was almost as formidable as that of Miss Buss at school. But the chance to try for the professional stage at all was so wonderful that she agreed at once. An interview was arranged. What should she wear? She tried on everything in her wardrobe. The trouble was that most of her dresses were becoming very tight across the bust. Instinctively she knew that 'prim' was the look she must strive for. Her dark skirt. The little green jacket. No frills or lace – not even her jewelled pin – a plain bonnet to cover her unruly dark curls, which she scraped up as tightly as she could. She looked at herself in the mirror, sucked in her cheeks, giggled and set off for an appointment at the St James's Theatre.

Madge Kendal, born into a theatrical family, had started her own career at a very early age and had little sympathy for aspiring young actresses. She listened to the eager newcomer without enthusiasm.

"How old are you?" she demanded.

"Eighteen," answered Jessie.

"My dear you are telling lies; you are twenty five at the very least!"

Jessie flushed. "I assure you I am not. I was born in 1861."

The bonnet had been a mistake, thought Jessie grimly. "My Father would confirm it but" …At the mention of her Father her voice began to tremble.

Mrs Kendal stood up. "Take off your bonnet," she said briskly. "Now walk across the room, slowly. Turn. Stand. Now back again."

Jessie did so. Mrs Kendal looked at her for a long moment without expression, then sat down again.

"Very well, Miss Millward," she said at last. "Out of friendship for your Father you will be permitted to walk on in the Kendal Company."

Jessie looked pleased, then puzzled. "Oh thank you, Mrs Kendal but ... I'm not quite sure about ... what exactly will I have to do ... walking on..?"

Mrs Kendal's eyebrows raised. "You will be required to walk on as, and when, I see fit."

"But ... but I ..." stammered Jessie.

Mrs Kendal rose imperiously. "My dear girl, you didn't imagine for a moment that you would be entrusted with *lines!*"

Jessie was shocked. "But ... I don't just want to walk on. I want to act!" she blurted out, her eyes filling with tears.

"What you want is neither here nor there, young woman," thundered Mrs Kendal. "If that is your attitude I fear you will be quite unsuited to the stage. You are totally inexperienced." She turned her head and gave a long sigh." I've never met so much presumption in one so young."

Jessie stood her ground. "But I have played many leading roles with the Carlton Dramatic Club."

Mrs Kendal shrugged. "Then in that case, Miss Millward," she said, making Jessie's name sound like an oath," My only suggestion is that you hire a theatre for a matinee and invite the critics ... if you can afford to."

The day that had begun with such excitement was now a disaster. Jessie left the St James's Theatre in a rage of disappointment. How could she possibly hire a theatre for a matinee?

Then she had an idea. She hurried along the Strand and round the corner to the Folly Theatre, where her Father's friend, John Toole, was playing. He was talking in his dressing room with his Manager when a distraught Jessie was shown in.

"Why, it's little Jessie," he exclaimed. "What's the matter?"

"I want to go on the stage," she answered, hesitantly.

"Very good idea," he beamed.

"And I want to give a special matinee!"

"Splendid!"

"And.. and can I have your theatre?"

"Of course."

Jessie's spirits soared. It wasn't so difficult to get on the stage after all.

"And when do you want the theatre?" asked Toole.

Jessie knew that all the male members of the Carlton Dramatic Club worked during the week. Obviously it would have to be a half holiday.

"Can I have it on a Saturday afternoon?" she asked breathlessly.

Toole's Manager grew pale with shock. John Toole regarded her calmly.

"Er – haven't I a matinee on Saturdays, Billington?" he asked.

"You have," growled Billington, giving Jessie a look that would have intimidated most young women of twice her age. It merely enraged Jessie.

"But, dear Mr Toole," she pleaded. "You are famous. You can have a matinee any day that you choose. My friends in the Carton Amateurs are all engaged in the sordid pursuits of their businesses and professions. And it's fearfully important for me. Couldn't you change it ? Just this once?"

Toole suppressed a chuckle. He looked at the eager young face. Lord, how quickly she had grown up. She was quite a beauty – and full of fire.

"Mm," he said thoughtfully. "I really see no reason why not." He turned to his dumb-struck manager. "See that it is arranged Billington, there's a good chap."

The Carlton Amateurs were beside themselves with excitement. Rehearsals were held each evening. They decided on a play already in their repertoire called *'Love's Sacrifice'* and, in addition, to show Jessie's versatility, they included in the programme a scene from a comedy called *'The Hunchback'*.

Invitations were sent out. On the Saturday afternoon, the small theatre was almost full and the matinee such a success that Jessie found herself inundated with offers from among others, the Bancrofts and Mr Toole himself. She would have preferred to accept almost any of these, however, she kept her vow to her Mother. It was with Mrs Kendal, who grudgingly admitted that the girl showed some promise, that Jessie began her professional career playing Mrs Mildmay in *Still Waters Run Deep*, and the ingénue in a translation of a French play called *Coralie*.

It was very different touring all over England from tripping off to evening rehearsals with the Amateurs, Jessie found, and Mrs Kendal was always on the lookout for mistakes. After playing Birmingham and Manchester the company arrived in Liverpool, where Charlie Millward was still well known as the proprietor of 'The Porcupine'. On the opening night of *Coralie*, his many friends turned out to support 'Charlie's daughter' and greeted her first appearance with tremendous but quite unwarranted enthusiasm. Jessie, who should have waited meekly for her Guardian to cross the room and kiss her, was so stunned, yet thrilled, that she rushed across the stage, flung her arms around the surprised leading man, John Hare, and soundly kissed him.

No sooner had the first act curtain fallen than Mrs Kendal called her to her room.

"Miss Millward!" Once again it sounded like a curse. "That was the most unmaidenly performance I have ever seen in my life!"

As Jessie went tearfully back to her dressing room she passed John Hare who smiled and took her hand. "I didn't mind at all, my dear," he said.

Jessie was also consoled by the notice she received in the theatrical journal, the ERA ,in which her acting was described as, *'Distinguished by singular naturalness and marked maturity, Miss Millward will make her place and long secure it in the theatrical world.'*

It was all that any young beginner could wish for.

Jessie cut out the notice and sent it to her Mother. The tour came to an end and the Company moved back to London to the

St James's Theatre. Rehearsals were long and arduous and she often fell asleep going home on the bus.

Mrs Kendal seemed bent on crushing what she could only see as waywardness in Jessie. "That is a ridiculous and quite unnecessary gesture," she complained, at one rehearsal.

Jessie sighed. "Oh, shall I ever be able to use my hands properly?"

"Never, my dear," was the reply. "You were not born on the stage!"

Jessie's West End début was in a one act play, *The Cape Mail* by Clement Scott, the critic who had so admired Terriss's early efforts. Also in the play was a young actor called Brandon Thomas who would later become famous as the author of *Charlie's Aunt*.

Another notice in the Era describing her performance as, *'Clever, sympathetic and thoroughly charming,'* did nothing to endear her to Mrs Kendal.

Fortunately, before the year was out she was offered a six week tour with the equally great, but more generous-spirited actress, Genevieve Ward. Widely travelled, Genevieve Ward was an American who had studied at the Comédie Française.

"You are very lucky, Jessie," said her Mother. "You will find Miss Ward much more sympathetic."

"I do hope you're right, Mama," said Jessie putting the last of her clothes in her wicker trunk. "Come and sit on the lid for me, girls," she shouted. Lil and little Flo sat giggling on the curved top while Jessie secured the straps. Her brother Harry dashed into the room. "The cab's here, Jess."

While her trunk was carried down the stairs Jessie slipped into the next room where her helpless Father sat. Jessie knelt beside him. "I'm off now, Pa. You remember? I'm playing Alice Verney in *Forget Me Not*, with Miss Ward. That's good, isn't it? I've learned my lines. I'll be back soon and tell you all about it."

Charlie Millward smiled his crooked smile and put his one good arm around his favourite daughter. Her eyes were bright with tears as she left the room and raced down the stairs to the waiting cab.

Genevieve Ward, although just as strict as Mrs Kendal, was indeed more sympathetic and, consequently, a much better teacher.

She soon saw that, although inexperienced, Jessie had both imagination and staying power, and that she learned quickly. The letters which Mrs Millward and the family received were full of the kindness that all the company were showing to the new recruit and the interesting places in which they were playing.

When they reached Sheffield, at the end of the week, a company outing to the stately home of Chatsworth was organised. A picnic was prepared and they all met at the Stage Door.

"There's a letter for Miss Millward," said the Stage Doorman, just as they were leaving. Jessie glanced at the envelope and when she saw it was not from home but from her Father's friend, Henry Irving, she stuffed it into her handbag.

"I'll read it later," she said "Irving's writing's so awful, it takes hours to work it out."

She imagined that he was taking a fatherly interest in her well-being. He really had no need to worry about her, she thought, she was perfectly happy and earning five whole pounds a week.

That evening Mr Vernon, the leading man said, somewhat impressed, "I hear you've had a letter from Irving. What does he say?"

"Heavens! I'd forgotten all about it," Jessie cried, fishing in her bag. "Here it is. Do read it for me. I can never make head or tail of his writing."

As the actor studied the difficult scrawl a look of wonder came over his face.

"My dear child," he began nervously. "He wants you to play Hero in *Much Ado* at the Lyceum – and," he swallowed, "and to understudy Ellen Terry! Do you realise what an honour this is? You've only been on the stage a few weeks!"

Jessie was unimpressed. She was happy where she was. And although Henry Irving was a family friend, he was not like Mr Toole, but much more distant and severe. She also doubted that he would pay her five pounds a week and give her the kind of instruction she was so enjoying. Consequently she wrote to him as only a naive, recent school-girl could have done. She was, she said, glad to hear from him. She would be in Town in a few weeks time and would call to see him.

Irving, from the Lyceum where his sumptuous production of *Romeo and Juliet* was playing to rapturous crowds, replied with gentle irony.

"Dear Miss Millward.

I too will be in Town in a few weeks' time. I will be delighted if you would call and see me. Yours truly. Henry Irving."

Genevieve Ward tried hard to make Jessie realise the great chance that had been offered her, and the other actors in the company never stopped telling her how lucky she was, but when the tour ended Jessie was sad.For the first time in her life she had felt free and independent. Even the family home now seemed somehow stifling. And she still had to call on Irving whom she had to admit she always found intimidating. She supposed it was because of the terrifying recitations in the firelight that had so mesmerised her as a small child.

When she at last went to see him, Irving sat at his desk. He rose to greet her.

"My dear Jessie. How well you look. Do sit down. As I said in my letter I very much want you to play the part of Hero in our production of *Much Ado* and also to understudy Miss Terry. As for further productions I shall need you for the ingénue roles. And also ..." he paused, his fingertips pressed together, "I shall want you to come to America with us."

"Oh," cried Jessie in alarm, "I couldn't possibly come to America. You see I live in London."

"Well ... we won't bother about America just now," he said soothingly."It won't be for some time anyhow. Now I want you to understand that at the Lyceum we provide everything ... all your costumes, wigs, shoes, gloves, everything. You don't have to concern yourself. Everything is included. Do you understand?"

"Yes," said Jessie, but in truth, her mind was racing ahead. 'If he's providing all this,' she thought, 'it must be because the salary is so low. I knew there had to be a catch somewhere.'

"And now," continued Irving. "What about salary? How much have you been getting with Miss Ward?"

"Five pounds a week!"

"Hm, "said Irving quietly. "I shouldn't give you that."

'I knew it,' thought Jessie as she watched him stroke his chin thoughtfully with his long, elegant fingers. 'It'll be all found and ten shillings pocket money.'

"I am really bound to Miss Ward," she said hopefully.

Irving smiled. "She tells me she will release you. She thinks it will be for your good. Of course I shan't give you five pounds a week. For the first year I will give you twelve and for the second year fifteen."

"Well," Jessie mumbled, "even with everything found ... well ... fifteen shillings is not much."

It was not until Irving roared with laughter that a wild idea came into her head. Could he mean pounds? He did. And if she would come to America he might manage twenty!

Two weeks later Jessie and her Mother spent a few days holiday in Margate. Jessie was determined to learn as much of the part of Hero before rehearsals began. The copy of her lines, with cues, was never out of her sight. She slept with it under her pillow and studied it while sitting on the beach. One fine afternoon, as she and her Mother were strolling back to the hotel for tea, they saw a handsome man coming swiftly towards them.

"Jessie. Isn't that William Terriss?" said Mrs Millward excitedly. "He's in the Lyceum Company I believe."

"I know," said Jessie as casually as she could. But she was as eager as her Mother to meet the famous leading man. As he came closer he looked with interest at the young, dark girl. He noted the thick curly hair under the brim of her hat, the huge dark eyes, the firm chin and the somewhat rebellious mouth. He introduced himself and they chatted about the weather.

"I believe that you are joining the Company at the Lyceum, Miss Millward," he said cheerily.

"Yes," said Jessie, bursting with pride. "I'm to play Hero."

"Oh … I don't think so," Terriss laughed down at her."You must be going to walk on. You're a very lucky girl, you know."

Jessie was furious. She tugged the script from her bag and opened it. "I am to play Hero and I can prove it. You see!" she cried, her eyes flashing.

"Well – 'pon my soul," exclaimed Terriss, glancing at the script. "You are right, Miss Millward. I'd never have believed it." He gave her a dazzling smile. "You're even luckier than I thought."

He raised his hat, bid them both good day and strode on.

"Goodness me, isn't he handsome!" said Mrs Millward. "I do think you were rather impolite, Jessie."

"I don't at all!" said Jessie She felt an odd mixture of rage and … and something else she could not quite explain.

CHAPTER FIVE

Since joining the Lyceum company and now established as a leading actor, William Terriss had moved his family to a more spacious home. Bedford Park was a new development of attractive houses, many designed by Norman Shaw, just north of Chiswick Common. When Terriss went to look at the area he made up his mind at once. "Just the thing for us, Isabel," he declared. "Good, solid property, plenty of fresh air and much more convenient for the theatre than Barnes!"

The house they chose, No 2 The Avenue, was called, somewhat whimsically, 'The Cottage' in spite of its being a rather grand house. Isabel and the three children, now aged twelve, eleven and nine, enjoyed the comfortable, rambling rooms and the extensive garden where the proud owner, on the day after they moved in, ceremoniously planted an apple tree. Bedford Park soon became popular with other actors, painters and writers, being far enough away to feel rural, yet with easy access to the West End on the District railway from Turnham Green station.

Terriss had a great many friends and, when he was not acting, was a generous host. Isabel quietly presided over supper parties where she watched her still boyish husband delight in discussions on a wide range of topics, including politics, plays in the making, (Pinero was a neighbour) clock collecting, or the latest fixtures for the West London Quoit Club of which he was an enthusiastic member.

After supper, cards were played, but Terriss's less affluent friends often found, on their way home, their losses mysteriously replaced in their pockets.His brother Bob, still a bachelor, was a frequent guest and his daughter Ellaline, already extremely pretty, would be allowed to stay up and often to sing. Isabel played her accompaniments and then whisked the child up to bed before the applause turned her head, but the indulgent audience could not fail to recognise another performer in the making.

Although a busy actor with many commitments, Terriss was a conscientious Father. He insisted on the boys being fit and strong. Tom and William were now capable swimmers as a result of their Father's unconventional tuition.The Lyceum having closed in August for a summer break, he had organised family outings to the sea. The children were taken, as they thought, for a rowing lesson. Once they were well away from the shore their Father told them to try a dip, hanging on to the boat. Protestations were useless. Not surprisingly they eventually lost their grip and he allowed them a few seconds of floundering before diving in.

Struggling, they found his wet and laughing face close to theirs, and his strong arms around them as they were shown, not at first how to swim, but how to float. He was so at home in the water and such an enthusiastic swimmer that they learned quickly. The only concession made to Ellaline was that, on her first attempt, she was tied on with a rope.

Summer was now over. *Romeo and Juliet* was back at the Lyceum, Terriss playing Mercutio, and the first rehearsal was called that day for Irving's production of *Much Ado about Nothing* which would open in October. Will Terriss was to play Don Pedro. Holidays were pleasant interludes, he thought as he strode along in his pale grey, tweed suit and soft-crowned hat, but it was good to be working at full stretch again. The weather was still warm but the horse chestnut trees on the edge of the Common were beginning to turn colour.

"Mornin', Mr Terriss, off up to Town then, is it?" The young man in the ticket office knew all his famous customers.

"Yes, Bob. Back to rehearsals!" William Terriss grinned, took his ticket and ran down the steps two at a time.

Jessie Millward had hardly slept all night.

"You must eat some breakfast," said her Mother." You've no idea how long he'll keep you." Rumours about Irving's rehearsals were already legion.

Jessie sighed. "I can't eat a thing. I am so nervous! Do I look all right?"

The clothes Jessie wore had been her own choice for her twenty-first birthday in July. Mrs Millward gazed at her daughter. How could she not admire, envy even, the handspan waist, the curving hips under the tiny bustle at the back of the long, dark red skirt, the full breasts beneath the trim, small, matching jacket with buttoned cuffs? She looked at the soft young skin on the curved cheek, the long dark eyelashes, the full mouth, and she hoped that Henry Irving would somehow find time to keep an eye on her.

Jessie walked past the Stage Door of the Lyceum three times. The fourth time she took one step in, peered and fled. The fifth time, Sergeant Barry, the Stage Doorman, all pink face and white whiskers, got down off his chair and came forward.

"Is it nervous we are, then?" he asked, gently.

Jessie nodded, staring at the collection of signed photographs of the famous on the wall behind him.

"Sure the Guvnor won't eat you." Barry smiled. "Although – I have to say you look good enough ... well ... what is it you're wanting then ... rehearsals? Well why didn't you say so ... through that door there. Off you go now."

Jessie walked onto the stage. It was in semi-darkness and there was no-one there. The auditorium stretched away before her into the shadows. There was a smell of paint and size and ancient dust. Coils of heavy rope hung from the flies and, even with shrouded scenery, the whole stage seemed much bigger than that of the St James's. She could hear conversation and found her way up a short flight of stairs into the Greenroom where a fire burned in the grate. The three actresses, no longer young, who sat waiting on a long sofa, looked very much at home, one was even crocheting. They introduced themselves and asked her what she was to play. On learning, they looked at one another.

"Well – you don't look the part," said the oldest woman. She examined her plump hands as if dismissing Jessie entirely.

"Oh, I don't agree," said the one nearest the fire, giving Jessie a watery smile. "I think she looks it, dear, but … " and her shrug spoke words.

Jessie drew herself up and marched down onto the stage again. It was so unfair. She wasn't a complete beginner. She had worked very hard with Miss Ward and she was sure she had improved. As she felt the tears prick her eyes she could hear someone else coming. A figure emerged from the shadows. Oh heavens! It was Mr Terriss.

"Hullo, it's our little Jessie Millward," he said cheerily.

Would no-one treat her seriously? "Miss Millward if you please, in the theatre," she retorted.

Will Terriss was startled. Had he really deserved that? What a little firebrand! As he took a step back there was a scampering in the wings and a small dog ran onto the stage. There were footsteps, sounds of laughter and Irving's distinctive voice. Jessie drew in her breath sharply and Will Terriss saw the fear beneath the bravado.

"Here's my hand," he said quickly. "Take it and you'll have a friend for life."

His eyes were an intense blue. Jessie put her hand in his and instantly felt as though she was being recharged with warmth and energy and courage. Irving swept in, noticeably tall among the crowd. Jessie was aware for the first time of signs of grey in the black hair which curled over the collar of his long dark overcoat but his glance behind the steel rimmed spectacles was as keen as always.

"Ah. Good morning, Miss Millward. Terriss. Good to see you." He paused and raised an eyebrow." You two are, I see, already acquainted. Mm... Hero and.. the Lyceum's professional 'hero' – so to speak." He smiled at Jessie."Will's always rescuing someone in distress." He moved on."Positively makes a habit of it," he called as he disappeared into his office which led directly off the stage.

"What did he mean?" asked Jessie.

"Oh – nothing. Just his little joke," said Terriss. "Here comes Loveday. We'll be starting soon."

Jessie looked with awe at the formally dressed gentleman with immaculate whiskers who carried a pile of scripts as though they were to be blessed at an altar.

"Ladies and Gentlemen. The Greenroom in five minutes," he announced solemnly and Jessie's heart leapt again.

"Don't be in such a fright," said Terriss. "You won't have to do a thing but listen."

And so it proved. Jessie tried to remember everything that evening to tell her Mother.

"Mr Irving read every part, Mamma. It was so wonderful. Every different voice. Only Miss Terry did read Beatrice. He began her first speech but she took over ... and their scenes together ... he plays Benedick of course ... they were such fun. How we laughed. At the end he gave out the other scripts. I'm glad I had mine already but ... he read all the lines so beautifully. You should have heard my *steal into the pleached bower'*... I'll never be able to do them as he did."

"Well, at least you'll look the part," said Mrs Millward. "And I'm sure you'll improve every day. Now bed and sleep."

The following day, Friday, the rehearsal consisted of a read through by the cast on stage. As the separate parts were written out by hand with only cues added, this necessitated a careful comparing of scripts. At the end of the afternoon Irving thanked the company, wished them a pleasant weekend and reminded them that the real work on *Much Ado About Nothing* would begin at eleven sharp on Monday.

From then on, Jessie hardly knew one day from another. Nothing, not even working for Mrs Kendal, had prepared her for the concentration that Irving demanded from his company, many of whom were also playing in *Romeo and Juliet* at night. It was as though she had had no previous life before the Lyceum. As well as rehearsing her own part she was required to cover Ellen Terry who, she soon found, was kindness itself.

When Irving first staged the opening scene between Beatrice and Benedick, Ellen Terry took Jessie's hand and walked her through beside her.

"You'll soon be able to walk alone," she said, as they sat in the wings together watching the next scene between Terriss and the young actor who played Claudio.

"What did Mr Irving mean the other day," enquired Jessie. "when he called Mr Terriss a professional hero?"

Ellen Terry chuckled. "Is that what he said? Irving loves to tease. Actually Will is utterly fearless. Once when we were rehearsing ... I can't remember what ... he arrived at the theatre soaked from head to foot. Loveday was surprised and asked him if it was raining and he just said, "Yes. Tropical downpour!" and carried on. Of course it hadn't been raining at all. Days later we found out he'd jumped into the river and pulled out a drowning child. It was very brave."

Jessie's eyes widened and Ellen Terry patted her knee.

"Half the young ladies in London are in love with him, my dear," she said."When Edy's little American friend saw him she declared ' I've gone such a mash on Terriss I wish I was hammered to him'." she laughed. "Only a child could put it so directly. He must know the effect he has but he doesn't take advantage ... just sails on merrily through the broken hearts, so ..." she gave Jessie a mischievous smile, "Beware!"

Jessie flushed. "Nothing was further from my mind!" she declared.

Jessie found the language of Shakespeare, although difficult, endlessly fascinating. Apart from Ellen Terry and Irving she listened carefully to the other actors, especially the older ones; Mr Howe who had worked with the famous Macready, Mr Meade and Mr Fernandez who had played just about everything in their long careers.

"Always remember, my dear," said James Fernandez when they were waiting together for an entrance, "if you're asked if you can do something, always say yes. No matter what. Singing, dancing, fencing, anything ... Just get the part and learn how to do it later."

As rehearsals progressed, props began to appear. The production of *Romeo and Juliet* came to an end, and in the remaining days, beautifully painted front cloths were hung and the complicated set for the church scene was gradually assembled. This was to be one of Irving's most lavish productions. Nothing was too costly. Even a well known concert singer, Jack Robertson, was engaged to sing. *'Sigh no more Ladies'*

Jessie and Terriss rehearsed their small scene together over and over for Irving.

Terriss, as Don Pedro, looked down again into Jessie's yes. Such delicious eyes he thought.

"Lady will you walk about with your friend?"

"So you walk softly and look sweetly,
and say nothing, I am yours for the walk:
and, especially when I walk away."

Jessie smiled. She'd got it right, at last.

"With me in your company?"

Terriss raised an eyebrow. Mockingly Jessie half turned away,

"I may say so when I please."

Terriss marvelled at the way she had grown in confidence.
Irving suddenly called from his chair at the front of the
stage.

"Miss Millward. A moment please,." and once again Terriss
saw how quickly that confidence could disappear.

"Oh Lord," she breathed and walked downstage, her
nervous footsteps sounding deafening to her in the sudden
silence.

Irving looked up.

"A very pretty frock you're wearing," he said mildly.

"Thank you," Jessie said, slightly relieved.

"What's it for?" he demanded.

"I beg your pardon?" she asked, bewildered.

"The frock!" exclaimed Irving. "What is its purpose?"

"Purpose? Oh ..." Jessie smiled at him, pushing back the
curls from her forehead, "Why I'm invited to a luncheon" she
confided gaily. "As soon as rehearsals are over."

Irving regarded her for a moment without speaking. "Go at
once," he said, grandly. "Go at once, my dear. Do not let the
rehearsal detain you."

"But ... but ..." she stammered.

"Tomorrow, however," his eyes blazed and his voice was
stern. "Come in your working clothes – with your mind full of
your work!"

With burning cheeks, Jessie rejoined Will Terriss upstage.
Tears that she had fought back flooded out.

"Don't go on so," he comforted her."Here have my
handkerchief, it's bigger. Come on – get your things and I'll call
you a cab." He led her into the wings ." He'll have forgotten
about it by tomorrow," he said, as they walked up the cold,
gloomy staircase to her dressing room.

"I'll never forget it," said Jessie, blowing her nose. "Not as
long as I live. I am so ashamed. "

As Jessie changed her shoes and took down her outdoor clothes, Will Terriss stood in the doorway watching her. She looked at herself in the mirror and sighed. "Do you think I'll ever be a real actress?"

"Of course you will!" 'What a funny little mixture she was,' he thought.

"It's my whole ambition," she said, "since I was a child ... but ... perhaps Mrs Kendal was right. She told me I should never succeed."

"Did she, indeed,?" said Terriss, amused.

"Yes. I'm afraid she never approved of me at all ... and yet ... do you know Mr Terriss," she confided, "she was most displeased when she learned that I was coming to the Lyceum."

"Well ... rather proved her wrong, didn't it?" said Terriss.

Jessie giggled. "I suppose you think you have done better for yourself, Miss Millward' said Jessie suddenly, with a wickedly accurate imitation of the renowned Matron of the Drama. "Personally," she continued, in Madge Kendal's unmistakable tones, "I think Irving laughable. I sit in the box and wonder at his success." Jessie's eyes grew even larger. "How could she say such a thing?"

"How indeed?" answered Terriss, looking at her with delight.

"And then," said Jessie. "She gave me one of her looks and said 'There is a type of gel who goes on the stage and whose only ambition is a carriage, sealskins and diamonds."

Terriss roared with laughter."And what are your ambitions – little Miss Millward?"

"I would like to be a great actress like Adelaide Neilson," she answered seriously." Do you know she once gave me a beautiful cross. I shall wear it on the first night." Jessie buttoned her cloak." Did you always want to be an actor too, Mr Terriss?" she asked, solemnly.

"Not at all!" he chuckled. "As a matter of fact I rather fancied the medical profession at one time."

"You wanted to be a doctor?" Jessie was astonished.

"Yes. My brother was a student at St Mary's. Mind you – he was appalled. He thought I should have stayed in India."

"India?" Jessie asked, amazed.

"Yes. I'll carry that for you."

Jessie found her bag and script taken from her as she was propelled towards the stairs."I'd already had a try at tea-planting in Chittagong."

"Chittagong?' Jessie echoed faintly.

"Yes, lovely place but tea-planting is even more boring than the Navy."

Jessie, hurrying beside him, was captivated; Irving's reprimand already receding.

"Yes," said Terriss." I tried that for a while after engineering you know. As a matter of fact I earned my first guinea as an actor almost by chance. And I didn't have to learn a line."

Terriss stopped, struck an attitude and the dusty staircase was transformed into an Ivy-covered tower in Birmingham as he described how he climbed it for overweight James Rogers. Jessie laughed. She had an uninhibited, musical laugh. She was extraordinarily pretty, he had to say. And he'd certainly succeeded in cheering her up.

"And then you became a famous actor!" she said.

"Ah – well no," Terriss skipped the last three stairs and looked up."I was married by then and I couldn't sit around waiting for better parts so we went off to try something else in the Falkland Islands."

"The Falkland Islands? Where on earth are they?" Jessie almost ran to keep up with him along the narrow corridor to the Stage Door.

"Oh, about ten thousand miles away. Off the coast of South America. Not a bad life if you can stand the weather. Terribly windy."

"Goodness me!"

"It wasn't the place to bring up a child so when my

daughter was born – she's twelve now – we came home on a whaler – when I think of it now! It took us four months!"

" And then you settled down and ,,, ?"

"Well ... not exactly." Terriss gave a rueful smile as they reached the Stage Door. He pulled it open and they walked out together into the noisy street."I tried horse breeding in Kentucky for a while. Couldn't fail they said."

"But.... it did?" Jessie looked anxiously up at him with her great eyes.

"'Fraid so. Frightful journey home. Oh look, there's a cab. Cabby!" he shouted, bounding forward.

As he handed Jessie up he grinned."But that was my last adventure across the ocean. Here you are."

"Thank you," As Jessie took her bag from him she said wistfully" And I've never been further than Liverpool!"

"Never mind," said Terriss cheerily."We'll be off to America before long!"

For a fleeting moment as the cab pulled away, their eyes met and a tiny sense of shock passed between them. Jessie sat back in her seat and thought she could understand why anyone might want to be hammered to him. Then she giggled, adjusted her hat and wondered what there would be for luncheon. She was suddenly starving.

CHAPTER SIX

The final rehearsals were to tax the entire Lyceum Company. Irving, aware that his production of *Much Ado About Nothing* was a potential winner, was determined that it should be as perfect as he could make it. He had enormous stamina and patience. If he thought an actor could achieve what he wanted by working just a little harder, then he would persist, and they would continue, hour after hour. There were differences between lrving and Ellen Terry about the timing in their scenes together, she forever trying to speed him up, he insisting on a more measured pace.

Terriss had trouble with a speech at the end of his first scene with Claudio. Each time he arrived at the dreaded line *"What needs the bridge much broader than the flood?"* he put the emphasis on a different word. An exasperated Irving stopped him yet again.

"Tell me, Terriss! What does it *mean*?' he finally demanded.

Terriss, with a cheeky grin, replied "Oh *you* know Guv'nor ... well.. it's poetry, isn't it!

Irving burst out laughing and the tension was broken.

Jessie was constantly checked and made to repeat a move. Sometimes she felt that she would never get to play a scene all the way through without being corrected. Three dress rehearsals succeeded one another, each lasting all night. Jessie found the elaborate, costumed processions which Irving staged, to be the most hazardous. Her long train and, in the church scene, the number of pillars which must be avoided at all costs, made her nervous.

The distance between each actor had been carefully spaced out, but somehow she always found herself, in a effort not to have her train trodden on by the actor behind her, moving forward too quickly. Once again it was Terriss who defused Irving's rising anger. It was almost five o'clock in the morning when he suddenly called a halt and, giving a shamelessly exaggerated imitation of Irving's distinctive walk, showed Jessie how to keep behind it. Irving laughed in spite of himself and Jessie breathed again.

"And remember," Irving told her, "that although *Hero* should not be tall, as you are small, you may walk as tall as you please. So, once again ... straight back and head high, Miss Millward ... if you please. Ah! that's better! Now let us get it right *this* time, eh?"

At the end of the final dress rehearsal Jessie was both exhausted and full of apprehension. Mr Fernandez stopped her on her way upstairs.

"Cheer up, my dear," he said "You are charming and promising, Jessie. And one day you will be a very good actress indeed."

"I just don't know anything any more," she said, turning away and leaning her forehead wearily against the cool wall.

"That's because you are tired out," he said, taking her arm. "And it's also because you've been frightened to death at rehearsals ... stopped and corrected again and again. I know!" He wagged his finger at her and smiled."But have you realised, my dear child, tomorrow night you can't be stopped or corrected? Think of that! You just have confidence in yourself and enjoy it. And the play will seem to have wings."

Jessie fastened around her neck the opal cross that Adelaide Neilson had given her so long ago and looked at herself in the mirror. She thought about her father and how he would have loved to see her. She thought about Genevieve Ward and her whole company that had been so kind. She mustn't let any of them down. It was a great responsibility. For a moment she felt quite sick with fright and rested her head on her hands. Then a sudden vision of disapproving Mrs Kendal made her lift her chin in defiance. The previous week while being driven to rehearsal she had seen Mr Kendal in the street and had stopped the carriage.

"Do tell Mrs Kendal that she was quite right," she had called to the startled man. "Here is my carriage – at three-and-sixpence the hour. I have a small pair of diamond ear-rings that my mother bought me and I've also got a seal skin coat that I bought from the Wardrobe Mistress at the Lyceum for eight guineas!"

She smiled, remembering the solemn way in which Mr Kendal had promised to deliver her message. Her nervousness was over. And, she thought, getting to her feet in her own dressing room, she was lucky to be on in the very first scene, it was so much easier than waiting.

She slipped into the darkened wings beside Ellen Terry. Ellen squeezed her hand and smiled. How tall and slender Ellen was, and how beautiful. Jessie took a deep breath as the curtain rose and all the warmth and expectant energy of a packed house enfolded her.

All was well. This was where she wanted to be. The gas lights hissed into brilliance, she moved forward with the other actors and in a few moments she heard herself saying, *"My Cousin means Signor Benedick of Padua ... "*

Much Ado was a triumph. The audience were enraptured from the first scene, but when the curtain rose on a darkened stage at the beginning of Act Five they watched in wonder as , one by one, the details of an elaborate Cathedral were revealed. First they glimpsed the solid pillars which soared thirty feet up and up to a crimson canopy. Then, like a painter's brush, the light travelled, glinting on the ecclesiastical lamps hung from chains of gold as it swept downwards, gradually filling in the details of the sumptuous scene. A silent phalanx of cathedral vergers in brown robes lit dozens of candles on a high altar, covered with gold cloth and piled with flowers. The light widened to show the massive but delicately wrought iron gates, then rose to show the religious statues halfway up the pillars and, finally, the stained glass windows blazed into glorious colour.

As soon as the curtain finally fell the house was in an uproar. The applause seemed as though it would never stop. The company took call after curtain call and Irving made a speech. The tired actors, as they at long last discarded costumes and make-up, allowed themselves a bright glow of satisfaction before the inevitable criticism which they knew would come the following day.

The company assembled in the morning and awaited their fate. Jessie was so tired she could remember almost nothing of her performance the night before but the excitement. One by one the actors were called forward, given gentle notes and dismissed. Jessie was left until last. This was it, she thought. She must have been so bad that he couldn't tell her in front of all the others. She began to shake. Irving came and sat beside her. He smiled. He seemed almost to be enjoying the nervousness of his, often wayward, young protégée.

"Nothing to correct, my dear," he said at last. "Very good; very good indeed."

"Thank you! Oh, thank you!" Jessie, ecstatic at his praise, brushed her eyes with her hand as she ran to her dressing room. Would she never be able to control her stupid tears? But ... what had he said? 'Nothing to correct?' Oh what bliss!

By the time she got home her brother had bought the first edition of the papers and was reading the notices.

"Listen to this, Jess!" he called, as he heard the front door close.

Her Mother and sisters were all assembled in the drawing room.

"Miss Millward has made her debut at the Lyceum," he began, *"and by her sweet and maidenly…'* Ha! Sweet and maidenly? if only they knew you!" he teased.

"Give it to me Herbert, you wretch!" Jessie grabbed the paper and continued, *"… by her sweet and maidenly personification of Hero has at once established her as a public favourite."*

"Well done, Jessie," Mrs Millward smiled proudly and hugged her two other daughters, who gazed at their sister in a delighted wonder.

"There's more," said Jessie, sitting down beside them. *"Her future is brightened with the promise of a brilliant career.* You hear that! I'm to have a brilliant career."

She jumped up and began to waltz around the room. "And … *Miss Millward's services have been secured to accompany Mr Irving to America next year."*

"Oh Jessie, you are lucky," sighed Lil.

"I know." said Jessie. Her face clouded suddenly. "I must run up directly and tell Pa."

The company settled into the routine of a long run. *Much Ado* played to packed houses from October to the following June. Neither meek nor suppliant by nature, Jessie found herself increasingly irked by Hero's character. She was much more in sympathy with Beatrice. Hero's calm acceptance of Claudio after he had jilted her, infuriated her.

"What a spineless creature she is!" she muttered to William Terriss as, after their scene together, they waited at the side as usual to join the others in the dance.

"I wouldn't have married Claudio if he'd been the last man on earth!"

Terriss's shoulders shook and she saw his eyes crinkle with laughter behind the mask he wore. She soon found that giggles were even more difficult to control than tears, and the actor who usually caused them was Mead. Mr Tom Mead was an old and very experienced actor. When Irving was young and struggling to master his craft, Mead had given him generous help. Irving never forgot and, when seventeen years later he formed his own company, he invited Mead to join him.

Mead had a wonderfully resonant voice but with increasing age his hearing and his memory became impaired. One evening, instead of Shakespeare's lines, he began the marriage scene with those from the Book of Common Prayer. As she knelt at his feet an astonished Jessie heard the great voice boom out above her,

"Dearly beloved ... We are gathered here...!"

Desperately she tried to stifle a giggle but Mead heard and once again roared "Dearly beloved ... and then in what he thought was an aside but in reality was as loud as the rest, he roared ..."And these damned amateurs!"

Anything unusual, however simple, was always heightened by the nightly backstage routine. One evening as Will Terriss led Jessie aside after their short scene together she stumbled on the hem of her dress. To steady her he put his arm around her waist. In real life such a moment might never have recurred; on stage it was inevitable. The next night, though she did not stumble, he held her again. As he waited for the reprimand which did not come, a frisson of excitement passed between them. Two pairs of eyes, so different in colour, slowly widened. From that moment, each succeeding night, the small scene which they played together became increasingly charged with feeling. The masks they wore as Don Pedro and Hero seem to give them licence to reveal, for that brief moment, their growing emotions.

"*Lady, will you walk about with your friend?*"
"*So you walk softly, and look sweetly,*
And say nothing, I am yours for the walk ... "

"Speak low if you speak love." Terriss would murmur once more as he led her off.

The masks off, they behaved with perfect propriety. For Jessie it was a delicious game. Will Terriss knew it was the beginning of something much more powerful and dangerous.

He had been married to Isabel for thirteen years and had never really been tempted before. He expended much physical energy playing games, riding and swimming. He was a restless, impatient but loving Father and husband. Isabel, though still a pretty woman, had grown matronly and treated her over energetic husband like an extension to her growing boys. She knew that his undoubted good looks were yet not the kind that made women cast him as a seducer. He was not devious but a fun-loving, golden chap that they worshipped from afar.

Will Terriss had married at twenty three on a whim and until now he had never questioned it. He well knew that many men of his acquaintance had a different Mistress every month but he was too straightforward a man to relish intrigue. He was also, however, a man used to getting what he wanted, and the realisation of just how much he wanted Jessie Millward was profoundly troubling. As for Jessie, she dreamed a good deal or had moments of intense excitement. Her mother watched her, worried, and wondered why her daughter had suddenly stopped talking about Mr Terriss at every opportunity.

But there were lighter moments. Towards the end of the run when Jessie as Hero lay in a dead faint on the steps of the altar, Mead, as he descended to her, tripped and did a spectacular, slow fall, landing beside her. Jessie opened her astonished eyes to see Irving, who had his back to the audience, convulsed with laughter.

Seeing her face he managed to gasp, "For God's sake – don't laugh!" It was the only time she would ever see him laugh on stage.

At the end of June, *Much Ado*, though still playing to good houses was taken off; their masked encounter and with it, their intrigue, suspended.

For the next two months, Jessie and Will, with the rest of the company rehearsed relentlessly during the day while polishing at night the plays that they were to take to America. Jessie was to play Irving's daughter, Julie, in an old play called *The Lyons Mail*. With her own father in mind she was much affected by the scene in which Julie has to part from her father. Consequently, to make it bearable, at the beginning of rehearsals she kept her feelings in check. Later, although usually so prone to tears when she least wanted them, she now found it difficult to summon them. But at the last dress rehearsal she was so exhausted and so overcome by Irving's performance that all the floodgates gave way. She burst not only into tears but had hysterics and fled from the stage. When she at last gained control she returned and waited for a reprimand. Irving looked down at her, raised an eyebrow and said, "Very good, my dear, very good. Er ... remember it and do it again tomorrow."

He was a wonderfully patient teacher and she now found that she was able to use her emotions. She was eager to tackle all the different roles but for Marie, the ingenue part in the production of *Louis XI*, she found to her dismay that the costumes she was required to wear had long been in store. At the end of the rehearsal as she tried on the faded, dusty dresses she pulled a face.

"They smell awful," she declared. "And they don't even fit. Can't I possibly have new dresses?"

Mr Loveday was kind but firm. "I'm sorry, my dear," he said. "The revival is only for repertoire. There is no need to incur any extra expense. And," he added solemnly, "what was good enough for Miss Bateman should be good enough for you."

"Miss Bateman?!" cried Jessie. "But that was twenty years ago. It's really not fair!"

Feeling the onset of yet more wretched tears she swiftly walked away. She did not notice Irving as she fled to her dressing room but soon afterwards she received a summons. Dreading a lecture for her childish behaviour she knocked on the door of his small and cluttered dressing room.

"Come in. Sit down. Sit down," he said, kindly. Jessie was so nervous she dropped onto the nearest chair. It seemed rather uncomfortable but she dared not move. She waited while Irving read a letter. At last he looked up. "You've been crying," he said "Why?"

Half in tears again Jessie blurted out that Mr Loveday said she had to wear Miss Bateman's costumes and could not have any new dresses.

"Oh, I think we could manage some new dresses," said Irving soothingly. Mrs Reid, the wardrobe mistress was sent for and brought down fabric samples from which a relieved Jessie was allowed to choose.

"There now," said Irving when the decisions were made,"Are you happy?"

"Oh yes," said Jessie.

Irving gazed at her. "And quite comfortable?" he enquired.

"Quite," lied Jessie.

"You're sure you are comfortable?" insisted Irving.

"Oh quite sure."

"Then, that's all right." laughed Irving. "Because you are sitting on my spurs."

The last night at the Lyceum before leaving for America was a benefit for Irving and among the actors who contributed was Johnny Toole. As Jessie stood in the wings watching him play a specially written farce – all the rules were relaxed this night – her tears of laughter were mixed with gratitude for the kindly man who had lent her his theatre for her matinee – was it only a year ago? It seemed a lifetime.

By the time the curtain fell the building was packed. Actors from every other theatre had hurried round as soon as they could and every aisle was full.

The cheers of two thousand people rang out again and again. While Irving made a speech and asked the audience to welcome the American company who were to play the Lyceum in his absence, his entire company, including all the stage crew, was assembling. Proud and trembling, Jessie stood next to Will Terriss. He smiled down at her, suddenly took her hand and kissed it. As Irving joined Ellen Terry in the centre, and the curtain rose again they all walked forward into the light, the band played *Auld Lang Syne*, and Jessie thought her heart must break with joy.

Jessie Millward as Hero

'Don Pedro' in *Much Ado About Nothing*

CHAPTER SEVEN

Dearest Ma,

Please forgive me ... the time just flies – we are so busy and I am still so excited I can scarcely write. When we sailed into New York it was all so beautiful and strange I thought I should die with the thrill of it. I hope you got my postcard but it couldn't really show you the half of it. There were steamboats everywhere and Brooklyn Bridge high up and sparkling in the sunlight . I cannot possibly write everything now Ma ... but I will do my best to keep a Journal for you and the girls – if I have time.

New York was all rush and bustle and the heat was truly terrible – what they call an Indian Summer.

Then on our first night it poured with rain and the hot weather was over.

You would be amazed to see how New York women dress, Mamma, they are so gaudy and they wear diamond earrings in the street! But it was all so wonderful and we were a great success. We had hardly arrived before we were rehearsing all seven plays – of course I'm only in five of them. My dresses for Louis Xl are lovely – and my Jessica in The Merchant is well received – and before we left New York we gave a special matinee for the profession -they simply adored Irving playing the horrid, decrepit, old French King Louis, after seeing his splendid young Charles I.

The hotel was so hot ... and the spitting! American men spit all the time. Imagine it! We had a special ladies entrance to the hotel in New

York – the other one was full of cigar smoke and spittoons!
Philadelphia was much nicer – and the theatre much better too ... But
it's getting colder now. We have had some snow. I miss you all ...

Jessie put down her pen. The swaying of the train made
writing difficult and truly there was so much to tell, she hardly
knew where to begin.

Bram Stoker, Irving's business manager, had already been
in America for several weeks. After the Lyceum company had
played Edinburgh, Glasgow and Liverpool, Irving and Ellen
Terry left to join him in New York on the eleventh of October
1883, sailing on the liner, *Brittanic*. The rest of the company
followed in a slower ship, the *City of Rome*. Even before they
had cast off, Will Terriss took charge of the great family group
of almost a hundred. It included not only the wife of the
musical director, and their twin children, but also, Will Terriss
noted with a certain wry exasperation, young Herbert
Millward who, at Irving's invitation, had come to chaperone
his sister.

Jessie was alarmed when Terriss took her arm and
whispered,

"It's the rule of the sea that if anything happens, it's women
and children first!"

"Heavens! Are we going to be wrecked?" She had looked
up the journey in her school atlas and the sheer size of the
Atlantic terrified her.

"I shouldn't think so," he replied, airily, "but you shall be
the first to be saved. I've a pistol in my pocket."

A few days out at sea, young Herbert watched with awe as
Terriss, for a bet, swarmed up a tall mast with ease and he
thought the Captain a real spoilsport when he ordered him
down. They had left Liverpool to the sounds of bands and the
cheers of well-wishers and after so many months of sustained
work, the voyage ahead became a delirious school holiday with
consequent high spirits. The other passengers were fascinated to

be travelling with a company of actors and soon found themselves the butt of a joke. Some of the ladies, on remarking how incredibly handsome Terriss was, were told that his sister, also on board, was even more beautiful but, being jealous of her brother, would never appear with him. Norman Forbes, Terriss's young friend from the days at the Court Theatre, was elected to escort the mysterious beauty, and Terriss duly re-appeared, thanks to a wig and gown borrowed from the wardrobe mistress. Now it was the young men who swarmed around.

"Is she married?" they enquired.

"No, a widow." Norman lowered his eyes, dramatically.

"How old is she?"

"Twenty five."

"Has she money?"

"She's incredibly rich!" Norman Forbes was in his element.

After the whole company had enjoyed the joke, the mysterious sister, who was beginning to be slightly uneasy at the increasingly amorous advances 'she' was attracting, disappeared below never to be seen again.

Once into the open Atlantic, all but the most experienced sailors took to their cabins for what proved to be an exceptionally tough crossing, and the great harbour of New York was a most welcome sight. Irving and his company, now reunited, soon found that the Star Theatre on Broadway and 13th Street was not exactly the Lyceum. They had not realised that the fashionable centre of New York was fast moving uptown, with the new Metropolitan Opera House just opening on Broadway and 39th Street. The crew unpacked the massive load of props and scenery. As the hundredweight of nails and screws piled up on the dusty stage, to the dismay of Mr Arnott the property master, and the ever solemn Loveday, they discovered that some of the ancient backcloths, including the one for *The Bells* with which they were to open, had not survived the journey and simply fell to pieces.

Another unforeseen problem was that the majority of the tickets for *The Bells* had been bought on behalf of a ticket tout, a certain Macbride. His henchmen, well paid in money and cigars to monopolize the early queues, were, on the opening night, boldly re-selling two dollar seats for ten to fifteen dollars. But Irving, with his superhuman energy, had managed in the brief week of rehearsals to be the guest of honour at important functions, where he had generated much gooodwill. He had also charmed the press.

In spite of the ticket prices, the pouring rain, and the difficulties of creating an atmosphere in a theatre whose doors opened directly onto the street, Irving's extraordinary performance as Matthias in *The Bells* worked its usual magic. Matthias, the burgomaster, whose conscience finally entraps him into confessing, and horrifyingly re-enacting, the murder which he had got away with for fifteen years, was a role which Irving had perfected. The American critics, although not unanimous in praise, recognised that Irving and his Lyceum Company were unique, and definitely to be seen.

For their part, the actors found the audiences intriguingly different, picking up as they often did, points that were unnoticed in England, while neglecting others, and bursting into spontaneous applause in unexpected places. It kept them all alert.

They left New York for Philadelphia in a private train. As well as eight coaches there were two 60 foot long box-cars, an enormously long, low-sided waggon loaded with scenery, and over a hundred and fifty wicker skips. Once again the company was a great success at Philadelphia's much more comfortable Chestnut Theatre. Irving, however, realised that he could not continue to transport these unwieldy sets to and fro across such great distances. He sent most of the more bulky pieces back to New York while the company travelled onward.

The theatre in Boston was the largest so far. The moment they arrived, the crew were set to building and painting replacement scenery, while front and back cloths were hung and a brief rehearsal was held for *Louis XI*, in which both Will Terriss and Jessie played. He looked every inch the gallant Duc de Nemours, Jessie thought, as Will strode into the wings beside her, adjusting his frilled cuffs.

"You know you'll have to speak up, Miss Millward," he teased her. "This barn holds three thousand!"

Jessie grimaced "Oh Lord! And I think I'm getting a sore throat," she said. "It's so hot inside everywhere and yet outside it's getting colder every day."

"Open your mouth," he demanded, unthinkingly. Jessie came very close and did as she was bid. Will peered down her throat. Then the blue eyes which made her heart thud looked into hers.

"Nothing whatsoever wrong with it," he declared abruptly and turned away. Jessie was miffed. Had she been aware that the thudding of her own heart was mild in comparison with the wildness in Will Terriss's, she would have been surprised. She would have been astonished and alarmed to know of the turmoil that surged through his body; of his overwhelming longing to crush that exquisite mouth with his own; to take down her thick, dark hair, and to lay his head on her young breast ...

"Ladies and gentlemen, stand by, if you please," called Loveday.

Will Terriss wrenched himself back to the French court of the fifteenth century, took a long, deep breath, and the rehearsal began.

The days shortened. The December weather grew worse. By the time the season in Boston was finished and the company set off once more, this time for Baltimore, the forecast was grim. Jessie and Nellie da Sylva, the young actress with whom she was to share the two-berth compartment on this trip, unpacked their clothes and stowed them as best they could.

The long train journeys were becoming familiar but Nellie was shy and found the lack of privacy difficult. Jessie agreed to use the top berth when it was lowered. Having six siblings, she took the proximity very much in her stride, although she still found it disconcerting that complete strangers frequently marched up and down the central corridor of the train. On their first trip, Miss Payne, who played Ursula in *Much Ado*, complained bitterly when she poked her head in curl papers through the curtains to remonstrate with 'this intrusion into a ladies' bedroom' and had her picture taken by a reporter. "And Jessie," she wailed, "when I want to get down the ladder it's always somewhere else. And when I call for the guard – so is he! And as for ordinary privacy … Americans simply don't understand the word!"

When Irving's eight long coaches reached the Harlem river; in order to travel on to Baltimore, it was necessary for the train to be transferred onto a special steamer, the *Maryland*. Aided by a tug, the steamer carrying the train progressed in stately fashion down river, rounded Battery Point and crossed the Hudson to Jersey City where it could now join the Pennsylvania Railroad and set off again. As the theatres in America opened on Christmas Day, Irving decided to give the company an early Christmas supper aboard. Jessie experienced her first Christmas Eve away from home while moving slowly down the Harlem river in a snowstorm.

After feasting on oyster pie and cold beef, and toasting absent friends and family, small groups of the company stepped on deck briefly to watch the swirling snow against the night sky. Will Terriss wore a fur coat which he had bought in Boston and his customary tweed cap, Mead could hardly be glimpsed, so swathed was he in mufflers topped by a fleecy hat with ear flaps, but young Norman Forbes, though his ears tingled, could not be parted from his elegant topper. The women, wrapped in every scarf and shawl they possessed, shivered at the eerie sound of foghorns coming out of the darkness. Elderly Mrs Pauncefort wore two bonnets, one inside the other. With gloved hands thrust into fur muffs, they all ventured out to breathe the clear cold air before returning to the warmth below, while the slow, chugging progress continued.

Once the train was back on the railroad their progress was even slower. A blizzard raged. The tired company sighed as yet again the train came to a halt while the driving snow was cleared from the track. The sound of bells clanging from distant trains disturbed their fitful sleep. By the time they eventually reached Baltimore they were so late that there were scarcely four hours to prepare for the first performance, late on Christmas Day. After the stage crew had worked their usual miracles, the exhausted company assembled and were not cheered to see a pitifully small house.

"We must strive to do our best," Irving challenged them. "It is the only return we can make to those valiant few who have turned out from their comfortable firesides to welcome us on such a night!"

From his first entrance as Louis Xl, Irving played as if inspired. Will Terriss was the most perfect Duc de Nemours, better than Jess had ever seen him and the energy of the entire company rose to match the two leading men. The notices were ecstatic and their success in Baltimore assured.

The snow began to melt and for the next few days the actors equipped themselves with Wellington boots, locally called 'Arctic rubbers', to enable them to splash through the treacherous streets and see something of the town. The next stop was to be Chicago. When Sarah Bernhart had toured a few years previously her train had been held at gunpoint on this line as rumours of the jewellery with which she travelled had reached the ears of local bandits. Accordingly the crew were armed. It was late afternoon and everyone was resting.

"Do you think we will be ambushed, Jessie?" Nellie called nervously from the lower bunk.

Jessie, in bodice and petticoat, sat up and breathed on the window, rubbed it vigorously and peered out at the frozen wilderness.

"I shouldn't think brigands ride about in this weather, Nellie," she reassured her. "Oh ... I can't sleep – I'm so tired of being cooped up in here and it's so hot and airless."

She lifted her long hair from her neck, stretched her arms above her head and yawned. She and Nellie were in the last section before the end of the compartment. Sliding her arms into her dressing gown she jumped down off the bunk and wandered down the central aisle. Opening the connecting door to see if it might be cooler, she was met by the most delicious smell. She tiptoed forward and peered through the glass. To her surprise she found that they were next to Irving's dining room and on the table she could see a large dish of small roasted birds. For a moment she stood gazing, her nose pressed against the glass, then raced back.

"Nellie," she exclaimed, "we're next to Irving's dining room and ... oh ... ! the most heavenly smells. You'll never guess what he's got on the table!"

"What?" Nellie sat up.

"Roasted quails! a whole dish of them!"

"Quails! Oh Jessie, don't. I adore them."

"So do I!"

The two girls looked at each other.

"I bet you, Jessie Millward, you wouldn't dare to get us one each."

Jessie's eyes widened . "Nellie, you amaze me. I thought you such a good girl."

Nellie blushed. "I was only joking really."

"Yes," Jessie giggled, "but what a lark!"

Nellie looked worried. "You wouldn't dare – not really. Oh Jessie ...I didn't mean" ... But Jessie had already gone.The quails lay in a glistening heap, heads curved round and skewered with a tooth pick. Their skins were golden, crisp and aromatic. Jessie took a handkerchief from her pocket and carefully selected one of the little, still warm, bodies. She was just reaching for another when from the far end of the dining room Irving suddenly appeared. He stood in the doorway staring at her. With a cry Jessie dropped the quail and fled.

Back in her berth she pulled the curtains, covered her face and moaned. "Oh! Why did I do it?"

"What happened?" Nellie whimpered, "Oh Jessie ... "

"I feel such an idiot. How will I ever look him in the face? ..."

"Miss Millward?"

Both girls froze.

"Hey c'mon." The voice sounded friendly. "Is Miss Millward here?"

Hesitantly Nellie pulled back the curtain. George, the big black conductor was smiling. He held before him a dish covered with a silver lid.

"Mr Irving's compliments to the burglar, Missee," he recited and with a flourish, he lifted the lid to disclose two plump quails.

Chicago was snow bound. No attempt had been made, it seemed, to clear the packed snow which dazzled the eyes, so bright was the sun upon it. The bitterest winter for many years raged across America. The company arrived on January 7 and on their way from the station passed a house where water to put out a fire had frozen in mid-air, covering the building in fantastical shapes. The thermometer dropped to twenty-five below zero. Everyone wore fur coats and hats to tour the city by sleigh. Chicago was being rebuilt after twice being destroyed by fire, and the citizens, anxious to prove that they could provide as hearty a welcome as anywhere else, including and especially, New York – packed the theatre night after night and afterwards entertained the company lavishly. Jessie lost count of the number of suppers to which they were invited; of the speeches and recitations that they gave.

Will Terriss, while making polite conversation, would watch her sparkling unselfconsciously beside some lucky young local businessman. He would catch her eye and her colour would rise but what, he asked himself, could he offer her? Tonight she wore a red dress she had bought in New York. Her dark hair was piled on top of her head and encircled with tiny pearls. She looked stunning.

But she was so young. How could he begin to tell her of his feelings? Lord knows he had hardly any opportunity – she was rarely alone. No – the sooner he got this out of his system the better. Dammit! He must just try harder. But it was so confoundedly unfair! At that moment she smiled at him and mischievously raised her glass.

The young lady on his left to whom he had been talking, repeated her question, somewhat querulously, for the third time. 'Well ..'.. she thought, ' Mr Terriss was undeniably as handsome as everyone said he was, but, he sure was absent minded'!

CHAPTER EIGHT

Though Irving was an exacting task-master he was also generous and perceptive. He knew that the tour was hard. The distances were great and the itinerary badly planned; an error he would not repeat with subsequent ventures to America. After weeks of shuttling by rail from Chicago to St Louis, to Cincinnati, Indianapolis, Washington and back to Chicago, the company had come north to Detroit and Toronto. It was the end of February and although sustained by their continuing success, they were all more than ready for a brief holiday.

After two evenings without a performance, an excursion had been arranged to see the famous Niagara Falls, to be followed by a banquet at a nearby restaurant. In high spirits they helped each other down from the overheated train into a clear, cold air that pinched their noses and grabbed at their throats. With almost no tourists at this season, Bram Stoker, as always charged with the Company's both working and leisure arrangements, had managed to hire every available local vehicle to transport them. Will Terriss, persuading Norman Forbes that the somewhat ancient omnibus would be more comfortable than the assorted carriages, leaped on board and swiftly took a seat behind Jessie and Miss Payne.

"Oh, Mr Terriss, I'm so excited," said Mrs Pauncefort. "But I'm also a little nervous. I've heard the Falls are dreadfully dangerous."

"Think nothing of it, dear," breezed Will. "Young Forbes and young Herbert here will be on hand to look after you, not to mention myself, of course." Jessie's brother squared his shoulders with pride but Norman Forbes, smoothing his gloves on his long fingers, looked less convinced. The sun came out to sparkle on the icy roads. Following the river the oddly assorted convoy snaked through a Christmas card landscape. When they came to the bend from which the first view of the Falls and the great cloud of spray which rose above them could be seen, nothing could have prepared them for the wonder of it. They left the omnibus to walk the last distance. The incredible tumult and incessant roar of the water as it hurled itself over, both scared and thrilled Jessie.

"Look, oh look how it changes colour," she exclaimed. "It's so dark and smooth until it plunges and then – all that boiling foam ... so pale and frothy!"

She found it hard to listen to the guide. He was explaining that small stones which were carried over had worn away the rocks into the frosty caverns at each side. Carefully she moved a little apart from the others. She gazed and gazed. She wanted nothing to intrude upon the sensation of the awesome energy which seemed to vibrate the frozen ground beneath her feet. It was strangely compelling. What would it be like to give oneself up to that incredible force? To be carried along so powerfully and then to plunge ...

She shuddered and glancing up saw Will Terriss looking at her. Suddenly, enthralled as she was in the elemental, all her defensive, girlish coquetry dissolved. She looked directly at him, vulnerable, questioning.

"Jess! We're going to walk round over there," shouted Herbert running towards her and skidding on the ice, "And later we can actually go down underneath the Falls. There's a staircase. You have to wear special clothes. What an adventure!"

Miss Payne declared, "Well, I've worn some costumes in my

time but this beats the lot," when those ladies brave enough were handed wide oilskin trousers, long oilskin coats, and hoods which tied under the chin. There was much laughing as they tried on different pairs of rubber boots. They joined the men and followed the guide to the crude spiral staircase which led down the cliff. An occasional rush of wind blew the ice cold spray into their faces as they descended. Miss Payne clutched Mrs Pauncefort who was determined to miss nothing.

"At my age, my dear," she shouted. "I might never get here again."

The men went ahead. It was very icy underfoot. Their guide suggested that the ladies be content to stand at the beginning of the narrow ledge behind the curtain of falling water. Jessie, struggling for breath, her eyes stinging, watched her brother, Will Terriss, Mr Arnott and several other men as they continued with their guide across the ledge. The sound of their voices was drowned completely by the continuous roar of the water which arched over their heads and boiled so far below.

Awkwardly they advanced. The ledge was narrow, the slate underfoot treacherous. She saw them through the spray as they stood for a moment gazing upward, pointing and nodding, smiling at each other. Suddenly a slate dislodged. Will Terriss's foot slipped. In a flash he was out of reach of his companions. With horror Jessie saw him hanging on to a rock with one hand as he tried to swing himself up. The ladies shrieked and Miss Payne covered her eyes. Jessie stood as if turned to stone. At his third attempt Terriss was successful and he was quickly grabbed by the others and hauled to safety. As the men rejoined them, each one white and shaken, Jessie saw that Terriss's hand was pouring with blood. She could say nothing.

The guide led him straight to have the wound bandaged and the ladies climbed slowly back. "What a terrible shock!" said Mrs Pauncefort. "Poor Mr Terriss."

"I shall have nightmares for weeks!" sighed Miss Payne, as they reached the top of the staircase.

"We must just be thankful that it wasn't worse," said Mrs Pauncefort as they dried and dressed themselves. Glasses of hot brandy were served.

" Are you all right, Jessie, my dear?"

"Yes." said Jessie. She buttoned her coat and hurried outside. She needed to be on her own. The raging waters were matched by the raging in her own heart as she now knew with a fearful certainty that she loved Will Terriss. The moment when he had hung between life and death had confirmed it. She had spoken so many lines about love, she didn't doubt these feelings for a moment. They were drowning her, crushing the breath from her lungs. She knew he found her attractive but this ... this was something utterly different. She must get herself under control. She must never let him know. She joined the other ladies, battling with herself to appear unflustered. 'Now we'll really see what sort of an actress you are, Jessie Millward,' she thought.

After such a day of high drama the banquet was a great success. Bram Stoker had ordered a traditional English meal: roast turkeys, chickens and great tureens of vegetables were carried in with ceremony and the birds were carved at the table. There were delicious plum puddings and unlimited punch and the whole meal was eaten with a wonderful view of the Falls through the large window. Members of the company made speeches and Mead, in his usual regal tones, rounded off the occasion by thanking Irving for his hospitality, his kindness, and his energy and courage in bringing them all from the Old Country to tour the New World.

That night when they played *The Merchant*, Will Terriss as Bassanio worked with his arm in a sling, Ellen Terry was concerned about his badly lacerated hand, but he had quite recovered his spirits,

"Absolutely nothing to worry about, Nellie," he reassured her, "just Bill's luck, dear. *Tempus fugit, etcetera!*"

"Oh Will, what's *tempus* got to do with it?" she challenged him, laughing. But Will sensed a change in Jessie who seemed to be keeping out of his way.

Before they left Toronto they were all invited to the Gala of the Toronto Toboggan Club, to partake of 'the maximum of enjoyment with the minimum of danger'. It was a glorious day. After a brief fall of snow, the sky was bright blue, the air dry and crisp. They travelled by sleighs, skimming past a frozen Lake Ontario on which ice yachts raced at great speed and skaters of all ages and sizes whirled about. It was a most exhilarating sight.

"Toboggan is the Indian name for a sled, you know, Jess," said Herbert excitedly. "It's like a small canoe with no sides. The driver sits at the back. Do you want to have a go with me?"

Jessie wasn't sure and in fact when they reached the great glassy mountain slope it was clear that only skilled tobogganists would be allowed to drive. Herbert mooched along at her side for a while until he was invited to be a passenger. What could he do? Jessie had declined and there were a lot of strangers about. She was a bit moody lately he thought, and he did so want to race a toboggan. Frantically he looked around and spied Mr Terriss also looking glum on account of his being 'hors de combat'. He ran across.

"Mr Terriss, sir, could I beg a favour and ask you to accompany my sister" he pleaded, breathlessly. Well, he thought, with a young brother's usual lack of insight, Mr Terriss couldn't race and she'd be quite safe with him.

"Absolutely delighted, my boy!" Terriss answered truthfully.

With her arm tucked in his and both their hearts plunging wildly he led her across the snow covered slope towards the trees. Usually so ready with badinage or a convenient lie, Will Terriss found himself tongue-tied. They walked on until the sounds of revelry receded. He stopped and faced her. "Jessie," he began, "tell me … did I imagine it?"

Her heart lurched so out of control it pained her. Was she so transparent?

"At the Falls?" he persisted. Still she said nothing. This shouldn't be happening. He was the Leading Man and married. With children. Oh God! what was she to do?

Will was desperate. He might never get another chance like this. He must declare himself.

"Jessie, my dear Jessie," He took her hand. "Our lives are too short to play games with each other."

So blue, so intense, his eyes held hers, demanding a response. Suddenly she felt the same strength and courage that had flowed through her on that first day of rehearsals, and so much more. How could she deny her feelings? And why should she?

"I … it's not a game … is it?" she whispered.

"Not for me. I swear it."

"Nor me." she looked at him directly,

"Oh my dearest, dearest Jessie." He smiled down at her young face, framed it its fur-trimmed bonnet, her eyes and cheeks aglow, one dark curl escaping through the knotted velvet ribbon. Were they observed? They turned back to look at the small, distant figures of the tobogganists as they hurtled down the slope and dragged up again. Brightly dressed actors who performed in a different drama with laughter, yells and cheers of encouragement. Reassured, Will and Jessie, in their world apart, walked on until they were in the shelter of a wide tree. He led her to the far side and leaned her against the trunk. An odd, sweet lassitude enfolded her. She raised her hand and moving a small overhanging branch, dislodged the snow which fell silently onto her collar. Tenderly he brushed it off then laid his cold cheek to hers.

Cold, soft cheek. Great, dark, almost liquid eyes. How they shone! He kissed her forehead, her nose, eyelids which fluttered under his oh-so gentle lips, and then the mouth which he had so longed for was under his own. Jessie was shocked by the wild, breathless pleasure of it. The sharp response in her body. Her startled eyes questioned his.

"Forgive me," he smiled triumphantly. "But can you deny – Miss Millward – that you enjoyed my kissing you?"

She did not reply but looked up at him, her swift breath making little eddies of steam in the cold air. Then, standing on tip-toe, she placed her mouth on his, softly, deliberately. He remained absolutely still for a moment then wrapped her fiercely in his arms, wincing as he did so.

"Oh," she cried. "Your poor arm!"

"It's nothing ... this is more than worth it!"

Later, walking sedately across the snow they rejoined the others. A bargain had been sealed. Only old Mrs Pauncefort noticed a certain but unmistakable something. She smiled and sighed. She'd always had a soft spot for Mr Terriss. But it wasn't going to be easy for little Jessie ...

Returning to Manhattan at the beginning of March the company took their second river trip on the *Maryland*, this time in daylight. They had left Boston at 2am and after a night aboard the train, most of the company were glad to stretch their legs on the broad deck of the steamer, which roofed in the sleeping carriages below. Will Terriss, his arm still in a sling, looked out pensively as they glided down the Harlem River. They passed the prison on Blackwell's Island. How he hated the idea of anyone being shut away. A small crocodile of women under guard looked across at them blankly.

"Oh those poor wretched creatures," cried Mrs Pauncefort.

Another floating train going upriver passed them with many a wave. Waterfront villas gave way to wharves and factories, with boats tied up to the jetties. Then the new spires on Fifth Avenue could be spotted against the skyline. At the far end of the deck Terriss watched the children playing. They had a long skipping-rope and were chanting as they turned it. Suddenly he realised that one of the youngsters was, in fact, Jessie. She had borrowed a woollen cap and was jumping and laughing with the rest. The game changed. He watched her as she ran and dodged, chased by the children, as she hugged them when they caught her. Their laughter floated down the deck. What a child she was. He felt sick with longing and sad with the responsibility of it all. Jessie suddenly felt surveyed. She shaded her eyes and looked along the deck, then waved and left the children.

"My dear," said Mrs Pauncefort. "I don't know where you get the energy?"

Jessie laughed, her face flushed. "I'm used to boisterous children," she said. "Don't forget there were seven of us at home."

The boat reached the end of the East River and began to change direction. Everyone came out on deck to gaze upward as they passed underneath the glorious, spidery network of Brooklyn Bridge.

"What a great adventure it all is," said Mrs Pauncefort, expressing the feelings of them all.

After another few weeks of touring, the company returned to New York where, reunited at last with the magnificent sets, *Much Ado* was played for a month.

The little scene between Jessie and Will became a nightly tryst. Irving watched and pondered. Jessie as Hero had a great success and the American impresario, Daniel Frohman, came several times to watch her performance.

"You must come back to America for me," he declared. Jessie was flattered.

The last night's bill consisted of acts from four plays including *Much Ado*. All New York seemed to be there, determined not to allow the Lyceum Company to go to bed. A grand supper party followed the final curtain with cheers and speeches and promises to return. Back at their hotels there were more celebrations. Even later that same night Bram Stoker counted his tired company aboard 'The City Of Chester' for the journey home. Long after the ladies were fast asleep in their cabins, Norman Forbes, his silk topper at an extraordinary angle, was among the very last stragglers to totter up the gangway.

On this homeward journey some of the company amused themselves by pretending that Will Terriss possessed powers of hypnosis, currently a topic of fashionable discussion. Jessie, nothing loth, was the chosen victim of those blue eyes. It was not the slightest hardship to gaze into them until she fell into a trance and obeyed simple instructions. But what began as a joke on deck to bemuse the gullible took a more serious turn when Terriss was formally approached to give a lecture on hypnosis in the salon.

"Dammit, Bram," he said, "how can I get out of it?"

Bram Stoker's beard quivered with amusement

"I rather think you can't, old chap," he said, "We'll all put our heads together and see what we can come up with."

Eventually he devised a short script which Terriss learned and Jessie, Nellie, and Norman Forbes were, in true Lyceum fashion, thoroughly rehearsed as 'subjects' until the demonstration was foolproof. It was much applauded.

Every day brought Jessie nearer home and the family she longed to see but she knew that it would, inevitably, also separate her from the man she loved. A few days before they docked, Will Terriss, playing poker, was chided for lack of his usual flair. His companions were not to know how keenly aware he was of the small figure leaning over the rail outside. He longed to throw down the cards and join her, but the great adventure was over. Reality was already animating the sepia pictures he carried of Isabel and the children and he knew that his career and reputation depended on his discretion. But his desire for Jessie Millward was as strong as ever and he was determined that somehow he would find a way to pursue it.

CHAPTER NINE

"But dammit, Guv'nor, we've hardly been home five minutes."

Will Terriss, running his fingers distractedly through his thick, fair hair, paced back and forth. "I ... I can't believe she's going back to America."

Irving sat at his desk. He peered closely at a collection of set designs for the next production. After a few moments he looked up. "Do sit down, Will, old chap," he said quietly,"you are making the dust fly about."

Will threw himself into a chair, chewed his thumb nail for a moment, then leapt up again.

"I know there's nothing for her in *Twelfth Night* but ... she's still under contract isn't she?" he demanded.

"She is." Irving returned to his papers.

"Then you might have stopped her?"

"Indeed I might."

"Then why? ... I don't understand." The blue eyes were bewildered, the mouth petulant.

Irving looked up briefly. "She came to inform me of Daniel Frohman's offer and to ask my advice – and my permission of course."

"You could have refused – held her to her contract."

"For what possible reason?"

Will Terriss sat down again. He looked at his hands.

"You know how things are.," he said, quietly. "How I feel."

Irving smiled at him, gently. "That's precisely why I encouraged her to go."

"But ... "

"Frohman had made her a very good offer. It's a leading role which will stretch her and I advised her to accept at once. She needed a little persuasion but ... "

"You actually persuaded her? I still don't see ... "

"Then allow me to enlighten you." Irving folded his hands. "My dear Will -you are a man of thirty seven – virile and handsome – none more so – but thirty seven nevertheless and with a wife and three children. Jessie is twenty two, has her career before her and, what is more, she is the daughter of one of my most respected friends." His expression grew sterner. "Someone who cannot protect her as he would have undoubtedly wished ... "

Will hung his head. "But I love her," he said simply. "God knows I wish I didn't ... but I do."

Irving got to his feet with a certain impatience.

"Yes, yes my dear chap. Such an unsettling business, love – is it not? But it will surely survive a short separation? During which time both parties will, I trust, be hard at work."

He took Will by the arm. "Come, my dear old fellow, do cheer up a little or ... better still," he continued with a sudden smile of inspiration, "let us take advantage of your mood to go over Orsino's speech."

He crossed to the door and held it open. "I've felt it lacked something from the beginning ... a certain ... verisimilitude ... yes, yes!"

Leading the way into the corridor he called triumphantly, "We'll go from *'Oh then unfold the passion of my love ...'* "

Will stood quietly for a moment, then said softly to himself, *"Then let they love be younger than thyself or thy affection cannot hold the bent, for women are as roses…"* His voice broke and he hurried after Irving.

Jessie sat at her open window gazing down through the leaves of a wisteria. The weather had been unusually sultry. Her mother and the nurse, who now came several times a week, had managed to wheel her father into the garden. He lay with his head back, his eyes closed. He seemed to be getting progressively weaker. She could see his hand trembling continuously against the rug which swathed his useless legs. Jessie's eyes filled with tears. Apart from her beloved Pa, she felt that she had somehow grown out of the family that she had so longed to see again.

She found her sisters childish and was unusually impatient with her noisy brothers. Even her old friends in the Carlton Amateurs, so eager to hear of her adventures, now seemed to her dreadfully conventional and naïve. Although still a member of the Lyceum Company there was nothing for her in the coming production of *Twelfth Night,* already in rehearsal. This was her first experience of 'resting' and she felt left out. The domestic and social round bored her and each empty evening was a torment.

Wanting desperately to talk to someone to whom she could at least mention the name of the man who filled her dreams and most of her waking thoughts, she invited Nelly da Silva to tea. The usually timid Nelly glowed. She was full of excited plans for the future. Far from wanting to reminisce about the great American adventure they had shared, she spent almost all the visit talking about Martin Harvey, one of the young actors from the Lyceum tour, to whom she had just become engaged. When she had gone, Jessie wept.

The offer from Daniel Frohman to play the Leading Lady in his next New York production came as a complete surprise. Mrs Millward, alarmed at her daughter's lethargy, considered her too fatigued to accept; but in Jessie's present mood her mother's counsel had the opposite effect from the one intended. Jessie knew that it was not tiredness that ailed her. If she could not be close to Will Terriss, she reasoned, she might as well be thousands of miles away. At least she would be working.

Irving, it seemed, agreed with her. He considered the role of Pauline to be a good one and in jovial mood said that the play, named as it was *Called Back*, was singularly appropriate. He reassured her that she should always consider the Lyceum as her home, and that as the company were planning to return to America at the end of September, their paths might cross. Mrs Millward was somewhat cheered by the fact that Jessie sailed for America accompanied by Daniel Frohman's partner, Dr Mallory, a clergyman and his wife.

Called Back opened in New York at the Fifth Avenue Theatre, did excellent business and settled in for a long run. The Lyceum Company arrived eventually but without Will Terriss. He had stayed in London to co-star with the lovely American actress Mary Anderson who had chosen him to play Romeo to her Juliet. The critics were divided on his performance. That of the Pall Mall Gazette wishing that *'Some method might be invented by which Mr Irving's brains might be spirited into Mr Terriss's handsome head.'* He added, though, *'The audience, however, admired the body and did not seem to miss the brains.'*

The public adored him and in their thousands, bought his image on a picture postcard. Each evening, sitting at their separate dressing tables divided by the Atlantic Ocean, Jessie and Will saw each other's images in the mirrors as they prepared for work. Jessie half hoped to forget him. New York was an exciting city. She was feted by many would-be admirers, invited to parties and taken on excursions; but she soon realised that her heart was always elsewhere. The first letter which came she read a thousand times.

'Mary is a good sort,' he wrote. *'I just say my lines and think of you. All the time, Jess. Don't stay in America. I love you to distraction.'*

And this when he was playing opposite one of the most beautiful actresses ever, she thought. As she read it yet again, her heart sang and she longed for the run to finish. But Daniel Frohman decided to tour his successful production and Jessie had no choice but to set off once more across America.

In London *Romeo and Juliet* came to an end and such was his triumph that William Terriss was signed up by the powerful Gatti brothers to be the new leading man at the popular Adelphi Theatre. Gattis had bought the rights to a new nautical melodrama called *Harbour Lights*. At last Will saw the chance he had been praying for. Now powerful enough to influence the choice of Leading Lady, there was, as far as he was concerned, but one candidate. In spite of the fact that Jessie had not played in London for two years, on her return to New York at the end of the tour she was handed a cable offering her the job. She replied *'Sailing in a week'*.

In the darkened wings of the Adelphi Theatre, Jessie and Will clung together.

"Don't ever run away again," his voice was husky. "Promise me."

"I promise. But ... I was so unhappy. I ..."

He stopped her mouth with kisses until she pulled away. "Please ... no more ... someone might come."

He grinned. "They're not called for another hour." He kissed her again and released her. "I said we needed to work our scenes first." He opened a large leather briefcase. "Have you had a chance to look at the part?"

"Mm," said Jessie. "I haven't got very far. I don't seem to do much in the first act except hand out jellies and tracts. It's not very exciting."

Will laughed. "Wait till the last scene with the wicked Squire – you'll find that energetic enough even for you! The production's top class. The Gattis are not mean. And they don't mind spending money on publicity."

He drew out of a folder the sketches for the harbour scene.

"Look at these," he said. " Hawes went down to Lynmouth for the inspiration ... when the sea was very rough."

Jessie looked at the detailed drawings.

"That reminds me," she said, prodding him gently. "What's all this about you nearly drowning while I was away ... and getting an award?"

"Oh, nothing," Will dismissed it. "Do look at this one of the cliffs. It's superb."

"Now don't try and change the subject," Jessie teased. "Herbert said you'd rescued some children. What happened?"

"It was nothing, I swear."

"But it was the Royal Humane Society medal, Herbert said," Jessie persisted. "It was in the papers. I don't imagine they give them out for nothing."

"It was six weeks ago. I've forgotten all about it." He smiled at her.

"Oh don't be infuriating. What happened?"

Will Terriss gave in. He sat Jessie up on the edge of a table where she watched and listened with shining eyes. "I took young Tom to Margate." he began."We were sailing off the North Foreland – stiffish breeze – Tom was doing very nicely." he nodded."I'm very pleased with him. Suddenly we saw these three lads bathing ... out much too far." He shook his head. "Usual reckless behaviour ... one of them got cramp ... started hollering. The others couldn't help him ... they were in bad shape themselves ... "

Jessie turned pale. "What did you do?"

"Simple, really." said Will, dismissively. "Tom luffed up into the wind. I lowered the lug sail, plunged in and pulled the lad out. Then we hauled in the other two – just in time by the look of them ... the sea was getting rougher by the minute."

Jessie slid off the table and threw her arms around him. "Don't ... I can't bear it." she hid her face. "I nearly lost you that other time," she whispered.

He stroked her hair then lifted her chin and kissed her gently.

"Well ... you did ask me to tell you," he grinned. "Cheer up!" He took her hand. "Let's look at out first scene together, shall we?"

Jessie dried her eyes and unfolded her script.

"David, that's me," he said, "has just come home from a long spell at sea." He laughed. "That shouldn't be too hard to imagine! Right."

He struck an attitude and began in ringing tones:

"When I saw the old church spire of Redcliffe as we came round the point, the salt water came into my eyes and I felt a great lump in my throat and if I hadn't shouted 'Hooray' I should have blubbered like a baby."

"Then I kiss you" he added in a normal voice, and did so. *"I can't help it, Dora. I've two years to make up for it, you know."* Jessie smiled. *"Two years and a month,"* she read demurely. *"So it is. That's for the month."* He kissed her. *"We'll finish the two years presently."* He kissed her again. "I haven't got another kiss marked there," said Jessie. "Who cares? Do you?"

"Not in the slightest," she giggled, kissing him again. "Where are we? Oh it's still you."

"Well, Dora my darling, are you glad to see your sailor lad back?"

"So glad I can hardly believe my happiness," said Jessie, with feeling.

"Do you think that I'm a phantom?" cried Will. *"A sailor from the Flying Dutchman crew and that I shall melt away? No fear of that my darling. Kiss me and see how real I am."* ... "Oh, good more kisses."

"You are real, David," said Jessie stroking his arm.

"I feel as though I could eat you," Will declared.

Jessie pealed with laughter, "Oh Will ... you'll have to speak to Mr Pettit about that line."

"I shall do no such thing," said Will, "It expresses my feelings perfectly. Oh Jessie, my little Jess." he stared at her with a delighted wonder. "What have you done to me? When you were in America I was like a lovesick boy. And now you're here ... and ... you do still love me? Say it!"

"I do still love you," Jessie looked at him. He was so strong, so confident. Everything about him bewitched her; the lithe, vigorous body, the blue eyes with their boyish sparkle, the handsome face, the beautiful mouth. How could she not love him?

"I will look after you, Jess ..." he said solemnly. "I will look after you and make you happy ... I swear it."

Mrs Millward tried once, and only once to dissuade her daughter. She might as well have attempted to turn the tide.

"Very well," she said at last, after Jessie announced her intention of moving into a small flat in Shaftesbury Avenue. "I would have wished it otherwise but ... we will not speak of it again. Perhaps if your father had been well ... "

"Don't bring Pa into it "Jessie was stung.

"He would have spoken to Mr Terriss ... made him realise ... "

"It wouldn't have made a jot of difference ... I love him. And he loves me." she added defiantly.

"No doubt," Mrs Millward, her face drawn and pale, looked with infinite sadness at the passionate young girl before her. "But what has William Terriss lost? Nothing. But you Jessie, you have thrown everything away and brought shame on the family. Oh Jessie! one day you will realise how foolish you have been ... but it will all be too late."

Will Terriss sat on the edge of the bed in shirt sleeves, his tweed jacket folded neatly over the back of a chair. Jessie still in bed, wore the white crepe de chine negligee that she had bought in New York, her long hair spread dark against the crumpled pillows. The room was long and narrow with a sloping ceiling. Muslin curtains framed the dormer window, from where faint sounds from the street below could be heard. They were engrossed in the papers which were spread out all over the bed. "Listen to this one, Jess," he said as he sipped his coffee.

"'The acting of the new play at the Adelphi is as well as it could be. As David Kingsley, Mr Terriss has a part after his own heart. He doesn't act...' Oh doesn't he? ... Ah ... *'He is the handsome, frank, sailor whose joyous laugh, bright eye and sturdy voice, etc, etc ...'* not bad, eh? What's amusing you?" he added as Jessie began to laugh.

She looked up from the paper. "Just listen ... *'Terriss's fondness for embracing the object of his affections 'Coram Populo' on all manner of occasions,'* she read, *'can be excused on the score of his ardent devotion getting the better of good manners...'* she giggled... "I told you there were too many kisses."

"Nonsense," he said, putting down his coffee and kissing her again. "He's a pompous idiot. Let me look."

"'These little blemishes apart,' continued Jessie, *'Terriss plays with a breezy vigour.'*

"Well, that's all right then," laughed Will, turning back to his own paper.

"Hey, Jessie. What about this? *'Miss Millward is an admirable heroine, graceful, tender and pretty...'* now there's a critic with perception."

Jessie leaned over to look. *'graceful, tender and pretty... upon whom most of the work falls!'* she exclaimed.

Will looked hurt. "What? Well, I'm not so sure about that! But ... " he threw down the paper and took her in his arms ..."exceedingly graceful, wonderfully tender and amazingly pretty ..." he murmured, kissing her throat, her neck and between her breasts.

Jessie thought she had never been so happy. She wanted nothing more than to give herself up to the overwhelming pleasure that she had now discovered.

At first she had been frightened by the intensity of her own response. But she had quickly realised that it was in this that he delighted. This wild, passionate young girl was a revelation to Will Terriss. When they made love it was as if they were on a winged journey together, to a glorious world that they alone shared. But she already knew that the afterglow, the long languorous return to reality was something she would always experience alone. Her mercurial lover would leave her bed with brief, loving kisses, already on his way elsewhere.

CHAPTER TEN

The devotees of the Adelphi melodrama came from all social classes. Night after night they packed the theatre to cheer the hero, hold their breath at the plight of the heroine, and berate the villain. Before their wondering eyes, raged thunderstorms and shipwrecks, gun battles and grand, Imperial processions, and adventures of unlimited peril. The new play, *Harbour Lights*, opened on December 3 1885, and Terriss, by now a real London favourite, lit up the stage with his dash and style, and the diminutive, dark-eyed Jessie was a perfect partner. They were accomplished actors who brought reality to often stilted lines, and their delight in each other was neither feigned nor disguised.

Jessie enjoyed the nightly struggle through the waiting crowds to and from the Stage Door, the baskets of flowers and notes of appreciation. One curious offering came regularly in the shape of a racing tip, twisted into a cocked hat, signed *'From your admirer'*. When these turned out to be winners, Jessie asked the Stage Doorkeeper what kind of person it was that delivered them. "He's a very shabby, little elderly gent," he replied.

"The next time he comes," said Jessie, "please ask his name and tell him that I should like to thank him personally for his kindness."

But on the arrival of the next tip she was told that her

admirer preferred to remain anonymous, saying ."She doesn't know me and she wouldn't want to."

For the hundredth performance the HOUSE FULL boards were set out yet again. Jessie, rouging her cheeks, was surprised when Will, who usually strolled in and out of her dressing room, called her name and tapped on her door. Meg, her dresser, opened it to find him accompanied by an extremely pretty young girl. Jessie took one look at the exquisite mouth and the bright blue eyes and, guessing at once who she must be, felt a shocked curiosity.

"I'm sorry, Jess ... " Will was ill at ease. "May I present my daughter Ellaline. She's in tonight and she begged me just to let her see you for a moment before the curtain."

Jessie clasped the very small hand in her own. "I am very pleased," she said. "Leave her here. We'll look after her. They haven't called the quarter yet."

Will gave her a grateful, apologetic look and left. Ellaline, at once completely at home, settled herself beside Jessie on the proffered chair.

"Oh, Miss Millward," she said eagerly, her voice as pretty as her face, "thank you so much. I did so want to come. I've seen the play six times already but well – a hundred performances – tonight is special, isn't it? And I do so love you as Dora."

"Thank you, my dear." Jessie, fascinated, continued with her make-up and took in the reflection of the delicate body, the long, fair, curling hair, and the small, retroussé nose which gave the girl a kittenish air. "But I'm sure it is your father you really come to see," she smiled, as she lined her eyelids.

"Oh no. Not at all," the blue eyes opened wide. "Well, yes," she conceded with the merest frown, "but not just him. Of course when my brothers came – it was the cliff rescue scene they loved the best – and it is fearfully exciting of course – but I adore it when you are saved from the wicked Squire. It makes my heart beat faster and faster every time I see it – even though I know you will be saved."

Jessie turned, amused and sensing a budding actress.

"Would you like to try one of these?" she held out a box of glacé fruits that had been sent round. "They are quite delicious."

Ellaline chose the largest. "Mm, what a wonderful flavour. My throat was a little dry. It's Papa's fault. We came up together on the District Railway and he will make me do my elocution."

"On the train?" asked Jessie, surprised.

"Oh yes," Ellaline nodded. "He says if I can make myself heard above the noise I shall develop my voice and then it will carry to the back of the largest theatre."

"I see," said Jessie.

"I would like to speak as beautifully as Aunt Nell, Miss Terry... oh, and you, of course. Oh, are you sure? Thank you, they are good, aren't they?"

Jessie, mesmerised, watched her lover's child lick the sugar daintily from around her mouth.

"When I'm eighteen I shall go to see if Mr Wyndham will take me on," said Ellaline confidentially. "Mother agrees. Mother was an actress once you know, Miss Millward. When she and Papa first met."

Jessie, already deep in uncharted waters, nodded.

"But now she has us to look after and – she's not well," Ellaline continued sadly. "She hardly ever goes out. It's such a pity. And the boys are sometimes very rowdy – and don't do as they are told," she confided, enjoying each dramatic nuance. "Especially when Papa's not there," she went on. "I shall never, ever get married and have children!" she declared. She gave Jessie a dazzling smile. "I shall be just like you, Miss Millward. A famous actress!"

The call boy rapped on the door and shouted "Fifteen minutes, Miss Millward!"

Ellaline jumped to her feet. "Oh I must go. Papa said I mustn't stay too long. Thank you so much, dear Miss Millward." She made a small curtsy, waved and was gone.

Jessie sat without moving, staring at her reflection. Her dresser, after glancing at her curiously, busied herself folding clothes.

"I'll just take these petticoats up to wardrobe, Miss," she said. "Is that all right?"

"What?" Jessie tried to collect her thoughts. "Oh, oh yes, Meg."

When the door closed behind her Jessie put her head in her hands, which were shaking. She felt as though a great, frightening chasm had opened up before her. She must pull herself together. The music for the opening sea shanty began as Will Terriss joined her in the wings. He saw the pale, tense face under the make up. "What is it, Jess?"

"How could I have been so blind?" she said almost to herself. "I never thought ..."

"What do you mean?"

She looked at him directly. "All those hours I must steal from them, your children." She shook her head in disbelief.

"Rubbish," said Will. "The boys are at school and will soon grow up." He stepped towards her. "I need you, Jess. I always will ..." he said softly, urgently. He put his arms around her but she turned away.

"She's so ... so innocent. She made me feel, soiled ... she made me feel a cheat." Her voice trembled.

He turned her to face him. "Don't ever say that. Of course she's innocent. She's a child, Jess. You're a woman. My woman. I can't manage without you ... please ... don't ..."

There was a burst of applause at the end of the opening music.

"How ironic," said Jessie bitterly as they moved forward automatically. "Night after night we tell our love ... in front of thousands of people and yet ..." her voice broke. "We can never declare it. It must remain a secret – shameful and hidden. Unspoken, unacknowledged."

"Jess, not now... God! I wish I'd not ... "

They moved into place on stage. Jessie sitting on a rock, Will kneeling before her. The curtain rose to a thunder of applause. Will wondered whether she would get through it. He thought back to that happy day when they had first read these lines. Now they would be so difficult – unbearable.

"Do you think I'm a phantom? A sailor from the Flying Dutchman crew and that I shall melt away? No fear of that my darling. Kiss me and see how real I am."

Will's strong voice pulled her together but his kisses almost undid her again. Would the scene never end?

"Oh Dora, let me look into your eyes my darling. In the wildest and darkest night I have seen those dear eyes – shining ahead – the harbour lights that told me of the sweet, bright, haven of home. Do you remember the question I asked you?"

"What question, David?"

Dora smiled sweetly. Jessie felt as though she might faint.

"Whether you loved me well enough to let me put on a plain gold ring on the fourth finger of your left hand. I've carried it in my pocket around the world and here it is."

Will pulled the ring from his pocket. Dear God! The lines could not be worse.

Jessie took a deep breath.

"Perhaps you thought you might see somebody abroad that you would like to marry," she said faintly.

Will squeezed her hands in his. They were cold as ice.

"I never meant to marry anyone else but you, my darling. Say

yes and you'll make me the happiest lad in Her Majesty's Service."

Jessie got to her feet. The audience waited spellbound.

"Oh David, it is so sudden," she smiled. *"You must give me some time to think about my answer."*

She took the three small steps and turned. *"I've been thinking David."* She waited for the burst of fond laughter. *"And the answer is ... oh yes!"*

She ran off stage to a surge of applause, tears pouring down her cheeks. As she stood trying to control herself she heard the end of Will's, by now famous, ring speech.

"Little ring, we're home again and someone else is going to keep you for ever and you will make David Kingsley's sweetheart, David Kingsley's wife."

A few days later Jessie returned home just as the young girl who came to help in the apartment was leaving. "Oh, Miss Millward ... I wasn't expectin' you back so soon," she said, standing at the top of the stairs and looking somewhat flustered.

"No," said Jessie. "I only went as far as the dressmaker's. The wind is so chilly."

"I laid the fire," said the girl. "Would you like me to light it for you? It won't take a minute. It draws really quick."

"No, Agnes, that's all right. You go," Jessie smiled sadly.

Agnes looked hesitant. "Miss..." she began, "I really couldn't... "

Jessie looked puzzled.. "Couldn't what?"

"Nothing," said Agnes, and bolted down the stairs.

Jessie closed the door behind her. Wearily she took off her coat and hat. The coat she hung up, the hat she threw onto a chair. It slid off onto the floor where she left it. She put a match to the fire and knelt watching the flame catch the paper, then the sticks under the coal begin to crackle. After a few moments she got to her feet and crossed to the dark red velvet sofa where she sat, her head against a cushion and her eyes closed.

Suddenly there was a scraping noise outside the window and Jessie sat up in alarm. When she saw a figure climbing in through the window she screamed and leapt to her feet.

Will Terriss, dishevelled, his hands and face streaked with dirt, jumped down into the room, a walking cane in his hand.

"It's all right, Jess," he shouted, "it's only me."

Jessie stood looking at him, furiously. "How did you get in?"

"The fair Agnes ... I persuaded her."

"She has strict instructions ... "

"It's no good blaming her," said Will. "It's your own fault."

"What do you mean?" her eyes blazed.

"Well if you've decided that I'm never to darken your doors again ... you should look more cheerful about it!"

"What on earth are you talking about?" Jessie cried angrily.

"If you had seemed happy, poor Agnes might have followed your 'oh so strict instructions'," said Will. "As it is – she's worried to death about you," he smiled. "or as she put it to me herself not half an hour ago," Will put on a most tragic air ... 'Thank Gawd you've come, Sir, she's in a fair decline'."

Jessie looked at him, sighed and gave a weary smile. "I don't know about a decline. You almost gave me a heart attack. What on earth were you doing hiding out there?"

"I wasn't hiding and I'm sorry I alarmed you." Will tapped his foot with the cane. "I got bored sitting waiting. I remembered you said a few weeks ago that the gutters were blocked so I got up onto that bit of the roof ... "

"You were on the roof?" Jessie cried, staring at him.

"Quite easy from here. Look!" Will turned.

"I don't want to look," said Jessie, "it's terribly high. You might have been killed."

"Fiddlesticks!" said Will. "It needs doing regularly that corner. Gets filled with leaves and rubbish. I just cleaned it out." He demonstrated with the cane, then his face changed. "Oh Jess ... why am I talking about drains and gutters?" He moved towards her.

"Don't touch me!", her voice was sharp.

"But I must touch you every night on stage." he said gently." I hold you and kiss you. I feel your heart beating against me ... but ... your eyes are cold. And the moment you leave the stage you won't even look at me. Jess, this can't go on.

"I don't intend it to," she said in a low voice. "As soon as this run is finished I shall leave the Adelphi."

"You can't be serious?"

"I'm perfectly serious. Frohman is in town and I ... "

"You're not going back to America?" he exclaimed despairingly.

"I don't know," said Jessie. "I haven't made up my mind."

"But who will play in ... "

"There are a dozen young actresses who would kill to play opposite you," she said harshly. "And you know it."

"But we ... we are a partnership, Jessie," he pleaded.

"Are we?"

"The audiences love us. They love you. Lord! You must know that."

How could he persuade her?

Jessie tossed her head. "They'll soon love another heroine. Just you wait and see."

"Aren't you happy at the Adelphi?"

"Oh yes, yes." For a moment Jessie forgot herself. "But ... " she continued. "Oh Will. This is the most difficult decision I have ever had to make. But I know in my heart it is the right one."

He spoke softly. "In your heart, Jess?"

Her face flushed. "In my conscience, then," she flared. She clenched her hands. "What we ... what I am doing is wrong. The moment I saw Ellaline I knew it."

"That's nonsense, she … "

"Why will you not understand?" cried Jessie passionately, beating her fists together. She stopped and turned away, trying to control herself. "What would you wish for Ellaline when she grows up?" she asked, quietly. "To fall in love with a man who is free to marry her, to live with her openly and honestly or," she turned to face him, "would you have her form a liaison with a man who already has a wife and children ... who must neglect them all to spend time with her?"

"That's unfair, Jess." Will was surprised and stung.

"It's perfectly fair." She stood challenging him. He said nothing for a long moment.

He felt empty and defeated.

"You know I cannot marry you, Jess," he said at last. "Before God, I wish I could but ... divorce? It's simply out of the question. Isabel would never recover. She's frail and often melancholic, she needs ..."

"I would never ask you to divorce her," Jessie broke in. "And ... in any case," her lip curled. "Imagine the scandal? Terriss, the tarnished hero!"

"You are very bitter, Jess," he said sadly. He had never seen her so against him and it hurt.

"I am just trying to see things with clear eyes, unlike you!" she retorted.

He stared at her, so small yet so fierce. There seemed nothing more he could say and a silence fell between them. The fire crackled and somewhere a clock struck mid-day. He waited and saw her shoulders relax. She sighed.

"It's not your fault," she said simply. "I chose to be with you and now I have to make the decision."

"Don't you love me anymore?" he asked quietly.

She looked at him. His hair was rumpled, his handsome face stained with dirt. Her body ached for him. How could she deny it?

"I love you with my whole heart," she said, quietly, "but ...

that doesn't make it right. Oh Will," she felt the wretched tears coming, "help me to do the right thing."

"Dammit, Jessie!" he cried." I can't even help myself. I didn't want this to happen. That first day ... it was only in simple friendship that I offered you my hand ... but now, Jess. This love I feel ... It is for you ... no-one else."

"But you are promised ... and not to me, not to me," she moaned, turning her head away. "You have your home, your children."

"Isabel and the children have my love. They always will." He moved towards her. "It can never be what I feel for you."

"If I could believe that." She had tried so hard to be strong and now she felt as though she were drowning, sliding, slipping away.

"It's true." He took her hands in his. "Oh, Jess. I know I'm selfish, but you fill my life with so much love there's love to spare. Must I really give you up? Must I free you to......to go to America?" He suddenly pushed her away. He looked at her wildly. "You might find a suitable young man there to marry. You could leave the theatre for a life of respectability? Perhaps that's what you really want? Is it? Is that what you want? Oh, Jess!"

They stood apart, each yearning for the other. Suddenly he moved swiftly and took her face in his hands. She could see his tears. "If that is what you would truly like, then look me in the eyes and tell me so," he said huskily.

"I can't," she sobbed, "I can't. Oh Will, hold me. Don't let me go."

He felt sick with relief. As they lay together on the sofa he stroked her hair tenderly. He covered her wet face with kisses until her sobs quietened. Suddenly he remembered.

"Jess, Jess," he said, sitting up "I've seen a cottage."

"What are you talking about?" she said, drying her eyes.

"A cottage," he repeated eagerly, "not far from Ascot. When I went down to George Edwarde's place last weekend we drove past it. There was a FOR SALE sign. Beautiful trees all around. It looked so peaceful ... so... so permanent." He smiled almost shyly. "I imagined us there, together, Jess. I pictured you in the garden."

Jessie looked at him, bewildered."I don't understand."

"Wait till you see it." He jumped up. "Oh, Jess, wipe your face, put on your hat with the red velvet ribbons and let's go."

"Now?" asked Jessie, trying to take it in. "Where is it?"

"A place called Winkfield," said Will, already making for the door. "It's not far," he assured her. "We can be there in a jiffy," he grinned. "If you like it I'll buy it at once." He searched in his pockets. "I've got the keys somewhere."

"You're impossible!" said Jessie weakly, following him.

"Here they are." Will was triumphant. "Come on." He kissed her, then pulled her by the hand. "Oh do hurry. We'll take a cab to Paddington. We can sort it all out and be back in time for the show."

Harbour Lights ran for 513 nights. Will Terriss and Jessie Millward as hero and heroine were joined by William Abingdon as villain and Harry Nicholl as the comic. In their continuing success and happiness neither Will nor Jessie would have taken particular notice of the supernumeraries who earned a nightly pittance making up the crowd scenes.

They were a mixed bunch, some quite experienced actors fallen on hard times, others, less talented, often earning money during the day as sandwich board men. Occasionally, for great military spectacles, real soldiers would be hired, and strictly disciplined by their sergeant. To the leading players, they were, inevitably, just part of the crowd. Will and Jessie would hardly have been aware at that time of a strange young man amongst the rest of the 'supers' in *Harbour Lights*.

An apprenticed ship-builder from Dundee, Richard Archer had always been stage-struck, often 'walking on' in his local theatre. When his Mother and half-sister moved to London, he followed them. With his strong Scottish accent and quite unwarranted opinion of his dramatic talent he soon became the butt of his fellow 'supers'. They took to calling him 'Mad Archer' This was said merely as a joke. They were not to know that strains of real madness, on his father's side of the family, were lying dormant beneath his delusions of theatrical grandeur, and that William Abingdon, the Adelphi's celebrated villain, would play a part in their eventual awakening.

PART TWO

CHAPTER ELEVEN

As an established company was gradually formed at the Adelphi, including a team of talented writers, one melodrama succeeded another, each more spectacular. William Terriss and Jessie Millward became the most popular hero and heroine in London. The cottage that Will had bought was renamed *Jessamine Cottage*. It was the perfect retreat, situated as it was at the end of a small lane on the edge of Windsor Forest. The hallway was lined with playbills advertising the earlier Adelphi melodramas, *Harbour Lights*, *The Bells of Haslemere*, *The Union Jack*, *Silver Falls*. The simple drawing room which looked out onto a large garden and the forest beyond, displayed more posters and photographs; Will and Jessie in costume on their 1889 American tour of *Scenes from Shakespeare*, and playbills from Drury Lane, where Jessie had been leading lady for three years. There were photographs of Terriss, as Henry II, and Irving in the title role, in the 1893 Lyceum production of Tennyson's *Becket*. On a shelf under the window was a small, silver-framed photograph of Ellaline, newly married, arm in arm with her husband, the impish young actor, Seymour Hicks.

The cottage was looked after during the week by Haddon, who lived in the nearby village of Winkfield. When Will and Jessie were playing in London he would get out the pony and trap on a Saturday evening and meet the last train from

Paddington. It was the one place where the lovers could throw off all restraint and simply be together, but often Jessie, accompanied by Lottie, now her faithful maid and confidante, came without him. The next weekend promised to be the same, but not for the usual reasons.

At the Thursday evening performance Will complained of a severe headache, an unheard-of happening. The bright blue eyes were narrowed in pain.

"You need a rest, Bill, old chap," said Dr Monks, who, at Jessie's request, had called at the theatre. "Take the rest of the week off. You've got an understudy, haven't you?"

"Yes," agreed Will testily. "But it's not good for business. I'll play tomorrow night and then take a long weekend – if you insist."

"I do! But don't come back too soon. Get right away. The Isle of Wight is bracing," he suggested. Will nodded gloomily.

After the Saturday night performance, Jessie sat removing her make-up while Lottie sponged her back. Jessie was now thirty-three, slightly plumper, but with her vivid little face almost unlined, even under the harsh lights of the dressing room.

"I'm glad that's over," she said. "Playing with an understudy is so much harder." Lottie draped a towel around her mistress's shoulders.

"I only hope Mr Terriss is having a real good rest," she said, rubbing vigorously. "Best thing Dr Monks did, if you ask me, makin' him take time off."

Jessie laughed. "Well, I'm not sure. When I saw them all off at Waterloo station this morning, Seymour and Will's brother were having the most heated argument. Why they both had to go, I can't imagine."

"Nor I," said Lottie. "I should have thought Mr Terriss's brother, bein' a doctor, was enough."

"Seymour is so fond of his father-in-law," said Jessie.

Lottie sniffed as she folded up the towel. It was clear that the young actor, Seymour Hicks, was not one of her favourites.

"Ah, well," said Jessie wearily. "They are all safely tucked up in the Isle of Wight for the weekend. Let's hope they've simmered down by now."

Lottie helped her to dress. "Let me do it," she said, fastening the tiny jet buttons on the dark green jacket, "you're worn out."

"I'm really glad I changed my mind and decided to go down tonight," said Jessie, swinging her legs up onto a chair. She handed Lottie the button hook, pulled up her skirt and leaned back, closing her eyes.

"Have you got the bags?" she asked sleepily, as Lottie fastened her boots.

"Yes," said Lottie," and the cab's waiting."

Jessie dozed on the train.

"It's a fine night, Miss Jessie," said Haddon, as he handed them up into the trap, "but dark as pitch. No moon."

"There's been some rain," said Jessie. "I can smell it. Mm. Wonderful."

As her eyes adjusted, the silhouette of the passing hedges became just visible. A barn owl hooted far away. Frogs were croaking in the pond at the bottom of the lane but fell silent as they drew nearer. Haddon slowed, then stopped. He bade them goodnight, and clopped off into the darkness, as Jessie and Lottie walked quietly up the path to the door. Lottie lit the lamp which always stood ready on the shelf just inside. Holding it high, she opened the door into the drawing room and screamed.

"What is it?" cried a terrified Jessie. Then she too caught sight of the three pairs of men's boots, standing in the hearth. "What on earth? ... ".she began, when a tousle-haired young man, wrapped in a rug, rushed in from the back parlour.

"Seymour!" shouted Jessie, "What on earth are you doing here?" Then she began to laugh helplessly. She fell on to the sofa. "I thought we'd got burglars," she said. "But I couldn't understand why they'd taken off their boots."

"I'm most fearfully sorry." Seymour Hicks hopped from one bare foot to the other. "We didn't think you were coming until tomorrow."

"I wasn't. I changed my mind. And Will and Dr Lewin? Where are they?"

"Asleep. Upstairs," answered Seymour. "And I'm sleeping – or rather, not sleeping, on the old settee in the parlour."

Jessie shook her head. "But I saw you off to the Isle of Wight," she said.

"Change of plan," said Seymour. "Pa-in-law said it would bore him to death."

Lottie sniffed. "Shall I make up a tray, Miss Jessie?"she said, dryly.

"Oh, yes, please, I'm starving. Sandwiches, Seymour?"

The young man nodded.

"Ham, I think we have ," Jessie smiled. "Is that right, Lottie?"

"It is," said Lottie and disappeared. By the time she had returned with a plate piled high and a bottle of wine, Seymour had smoothed his hair, found some slippers and seemed perfectly at ease.

"All quiet upstairs, Miss Jessie," said Lottie with a small smile.. "Will that be all?"

"Yes. Yes, Lottie and thank you. Goodnight." Jessie poured two glasses of wine and lay back, her head against the cushions. Seymour helped himself to a sandwich. With his small head and pointed chin, he had an ageless, elfin quality, although he was in his mid twenties.

"This is just the ticket," he said, munching away. "Still packin' them in, Jessie?"

"We are," answered Jessie. "I love the Adelphi. I'm glad to be back. America is wonderful but such hard work and it takes so long just getting from one side to the other."

"Don't I just know it!" exclaimed Seymour. "When I did my first tour with Mrs Kendal I thought it would never end."

Jessie pulled a face. "I'm not surprised," she said.

"But didn't Irving start in San Francisco this time?" asked Seymour, downing his wine and pouring another. He was really enjoying this unexpected supper. Jessie was such a sport and he didn't often have the chance for a good chat.

"Yes," laughed Jessie, "But we were so late getting there from New York, poor old Bram was having a fit. By the time we got to Cheyenne he was almost hysterical. 'We're two hours behind schedule, Terriss,' he shouted. 'And the Rockies still to climb.'"

"What did he expect Pa to do about it?" asked Seymour.

Jessie shrugged. "All I can say for certain is that Will just disappeared. It was only afterwards that he told me that he had bribed the driver to let him take over."

Seymour's jaw dropped. "Not to drive the train?"

"I'll never know," smiled Jessie. "But we certainly put on speed. We stopped at the very top to take on water and there was a notice saying 'THE SUMMIT OF THE ROCKIES' and we all hung out of the windows and cheered."

Seymour clapped his hands in delight.

"And as for going down the other side," Jessie continued. "I thought we would leap off the rails. It was so exciting."

"Sounds absolutely terrifying, to me," said Seymour. "More wine, Jessie?"

"Just a little. Thank you. But the audiences were wonderful. I'll never forget the roar that went up for Irving." Jessie smiled at the memory. "And I hear you had quite a hit in *Cinderella*, Seymour."

Seymour leaned forward, his hands clasped between his knees. "As Ugly Sister, you mean?" he grinned. "They actually praised my dancing. Everyone knows I can't dance. The critics were kindness itself but ... my fellow thespians ... !" He lifted his eyebrows and rolled his eyes upwards. "and all because I borrowed the odd idea, here and there, you know."

"What did they say, Seymour?" teased Jessie.

"Padlock your gags, folks!" said Seymour, in a heavy transatlantic accent. "Nail down everything you have. 'Stealmore Tricks' is in town!"

Jessie laughed. "Seymour I'm worn out. I must go to bed. Are you sure you have enough blankets?"

"Quite, thank you," he answered. "Do you mind if I finish off these sandwiches? They are awfully good."

The next morning was cloudless. Followed by Lottie with her arms full of cushions, Jessie came down into the garden. She wore a blue and white cotton skirt, a soft white muslin blouse and around her shoulders she had wrapped a flowered shawl in fine wool. She gathered up the corner and held it to her face. "This still smells of the lavender." she said. "What a heavenly morning. So peaceful."

As Lottie arranged the cushions on the garden chairs suddenly the sound of raised men's voices could be heard approaching. They turned to see Seymour and Dr Bob Lewin, trying to manoeuvre Will Terriss on a wicker chaise longue, through the back door.

"Don't rush so, boy," growled Bob Lewin.

"Back up a bit, then. That's the ticket," cried Seymour.

"I can perfectly well, walk!" exploded Will.

Lottie looked amused. "Well, it was peaceful,"she murmured.

"You're to rest!" cried Seymour. "Doctor's orders."

"I'm the doctor, young man," barked Bob Lewin.

"Stop it, you two," shouted Will. "This is all nonsense. Jess. Jess, tell them it's nonsense."

Jessie walked across the grass. "I shall do no such thing," she said calmly. "You were ordered to rest, and, since you've chosen to come here, I shall make sure that you do. Put him down over there. Under that tree. Now," she rearranged his blanket, "I don't want another word out of you until lunchtime."

Will took her hand and kissed it. "Yes, Nurse," he said fondly, and closed his eyes. She stood for a moment looking down at him. The still handsome face was heavier and paler than usual, and lines of strain were etched on his brow. Quietly she rejoined the other two men. Bob Lewin apologised for their having arrived so inopportunely. Seven years older than Will and heavily built, he was rather like an amiable bear, Jessie decided.

"I don't pretend to understand the theatre," he said solemnly. "I was most discouraging to poor Will. I was clearly no judge, but it always seemed to me such a ... a disreputable profession."

"Disreputable!" cried Seymour. "I have to tell you, sir, that to an actor, his reputation is all!"

"I'm sorry," spluttered Bob Lewin, "I didn't mean to imply ... "

"That's quite all right, sir. I can tell you it's jolly difficult maintaining any reputation whatsoever on an empty stomach," said Seymour, with a tragic expression. "I started on the princely salary of nine shillings a week."

"God bless my soul!" said Bob Lewin, truly shocked.

"Yes," continued Seymour, much enjoying himself, "forced to leave home without a bob or a blessing but .... I am happy to say that my family are now reconciled ... quite proud of my modest success. We should all be proud of our profession now that the Guv'nor has been honoured."

Bob Lewin looked bewildered.

"Have you not heard?" asked Seymour. "Henry Irving has just been knighted."

"Isn't it wonderful," said Jessie. "I sent him a telegram at once and he replied 'THOUSAND THANKS FOR CONGRATULATIONS BUT ONLY A NIGHTLY KNIGHT.'

"That's one in the eye for that dreadful Irishman, Shaw," said Seymour. "What does he know about the theatre? He's a music critic."

"I'm told he writes himself," said Jessie.

"Huh!" scoffed Seymour. "Boring, wordy stuff. Sort of rubbish they do at the Independent Theatre Society. Nobody wants to listen to it. You mark my words, the name of Sir Henry Irving will go down in the great annals of England while no-one will even remember Mr Shaw."

"Well," said Jessie. "Miss Terry seems to think he has promise."

"He just flatters her," replied Seymour. "Fancies himself no end with actresses. I've told my Ellaline to give him a wide berth, I can tell you."

"And how is Ellaline managing without her devoted husband this weekend?" asked Jessie.

"She's gone down to George Edwardes's place – near Ascot."

"But that's hardly any distance," said Jessie. " You could borrow Will's bicycle."

"But what about looking after .... ?" Seymour indicated Will, asleep. "And … I was rather hoping he might cast an eye on this …" He took a script from his pocket.

"Oh no," said Jessie firmly. "No scripts. Not this weekend. Please do feel free to go. We can manage perfectly well, can't we, Dr Lewin?"

"Oh, I'm sure we can," replied Bob Lewin, trying not to look too relieved.

"Well, if you're positive," said Seymour leaping up.

As they watched him wobble off up the lane, Lottie came out with a tray. She glanced down at Will as she passed. "Sleeping like a baby," she said. "I've brought you some lemonade."

"Thank you, Lottie." Jessie poured a glass. "Do try some, Dr Lewin. It's a special recipe. Seymour's gone to see his wife, Lottie," she added.

"No bad thing, if you ask me," said Lottie and went back to the house. Jessie and Bob Lewin sat in a companionable silence. The air grew warmer and a blackbird trilled in the hedge behind them.

"I believe Mr Hicks is playing at the Gaiety," said Bob. "Or so I understand. He talks so quickly and I know so little about the theatre.

"He's a dear, really," said Jessie. "And quite a talented writer too."

"I'm sure he is," said Bob Lewin. He looked at Jessie, her dark, glossy hair shining in the sunlight, her full breasts beneath the thin muslin blouse, her narrow waist, and he thought how lucky his brother was.

"He's working on a play for the Adelphi at the moment. Will thinks it's very promising," said Jessie. "It's based on the Dreyfus case – with the officer, of course, innocent of treason."

"Dreadful business," exclaimed Bob Lewin. "Scandalous. Never have happened in England!"

Jessie hid a smile. "Well, it will certainly be topical," she said, "and, we hope, with a good part for Will." Her face clouded and she hesitated, twisting the edge of her shawl. "Dr Lewin," she continued. "He has been overdoing it, hasn't he?" she asked. "I've never known him miss a performance before." Bob Lewin could see her concern.

"Of course," she continued, "he's hardly had a break since he left the Lyceum but ... sometimes I feel ... ," she looked away, biting her lip.

'Such a delicious lip,' he thought. "What is it, my dear?" he asked gently.

"I feel guilty, I suppose." she said. "He does too much. All his work and then he tries to spend time with me and ... at Bedford Park ... with the boys, too ... it is not easy."

He saw her eyes begin to brim with tears. She got up abruptly and walked across the lawn towards a bed of lupins underneath an arch of pink roses. Bob slowly joined her.

"That's 'Zepherine Drouhin', I believe," he said.

She turned. "You know about roses?"

"Only a little, I'm afraid," he smiled. "I would like to grow them but I have only a small garden in Paddington, Miss Millward."

"Jessie, please,"

"As you wish," He paused and looked at her intently. "My

dear, I'm just a crusty old bachelor and not good at putting my feelings into words, but you must not reproach yourself. I know how much you mean to my brother."

"Thank you," said Jessie, quietly.

"Won't you sit down again?" He led her back to the seat. "I was at Bedford Park, myself last week," he said. "Mrs Terriss is very frail."

"I understand that she has been so for some time," said Jessie, uneasily.

Bob Lewin held her gaze determinedly.

"Of course, she has not enjoyed good health for many years, and she has become increasingly reclusive but … this time I fear that it is more serious."

Jessie stared at him.

"It is my opinion," he continued, "that she has not long to live."

Jessie sat quite still. The shock and the succeeding turmoil of emotions stunned her.

"I had no idea," she said, at last. "How ... how long?"

"A year perhaps. Two at the most."

"Does Will know?"

He shook his head. "She does not wish it."

"Then why did you tell me?" cried Jessie, trying to make sense of it all.

"I thought it only right that you should know," said Bob Lewin, simply. He took her hand and held it for a minute. "Your love and support will mean everything to him now."

Jessie looked out across her garden. It was at its most beautiful at this time of the year. They had planned it together, she and Will.

"He will always have both," she said tremulously. "Thank you. Thank you for telling me."

"Jess!" It was Will's voice. Bob Lewin strode across the grass to where his brother lay stretching and yawning beneath the tree.

"I don't need to ask how you are," said Bob. The blue eyes were clear, the lines of strain quite gone.

Will sprang to his feet."Feel marvellous," he said. "A new man, Bob. Power of sleep, eh? Better than all your medic's remedies. Where's young Seymour?"

"He rode off on your bicycle."

"Where on earth to?"

"He's gone over to George's, to see Ellaline," called Jessie, still struggling to regain her composure.

"Well, that's the last we'll see of him," said Will. "Never mind. What a glorious day. I feel like celebrating. What about going to Windsor for lunch, Jessie? We'll have champagne! What do you say to that, old chap?"

Bob Lewin laughed. "Unwarranted extravagance is what I say but you won't listen to me. You never do."

Will put one arm affectionately around his brother and the other round Jessie.

"Quite right!" he said. "Haddon! Haddon!" he shouted. "Get out the trap, there's a good fellow. We're all going to Windsor for lunch."

Jessie Millward

William Terriss

CHAPTER TWELVE

In the following months Jessie had little time to brood over Bob Lewin's news. One melodrama succeeded another. *The Girl I Left Behind Me* was followed immediately by *The Swordsman's Daughter*. She and Will were also both involved with George Edwardes in the development of Seymour Hick's new play which they hoped to present next, and had decided to call *One of the Best*.

But often at night when she lay alone, memories of that summer afternoon among the roses at Jessamine Cottage would return. Sleep evading her, she would turn restlessly, and wonder about the future. How long would Isabel live and how would her death affect Will? Would they eventually marry? Would he in fact, want to marry her, after all this time? She was not, she reminded herself ruefully, the wide-eyed, fresh, young ingenue with whom he had first fallen in love. She knew he loved her still but … marriage … ? Her thoughts, ever inconclusive, would turn and turn until at last she fell into a troubled sleep.

Sometimes she tried to picture herself and Will growing old and respectable together. Sir William and Lady Terriss ? Why not? Imagine, after all this time, being received in polite society! At least her mother would be content. Then she would guiltily rein in her idle dreams and think of the frail woman whose life was coming to a close, and of the sadness her dying would bring to her children. Ellaline had Seymour to comfort her, but young Tom Terriss, whom she liked and who accepted her was, she knew, devoted to his mother.

Seymour Hicks was delighted with the reviews for *One of the Best*. The Dreyfus Case was still much discussed at the time and Terriss's portrayal of the wrongly accused Lieutenant Keppel of the 42nd Highlanders was a triumph. Especially powerful was the degradation scene, a brilliantly staged military spectacle when the gallant officer was stripped of his medals, and which Terriss played with a moving dignity and sincerity. Jessie's role was also heavy and dramatic.

The villain was, as usual, played by Billy Abingdon, who for the past seven years had become very much a part of the Adelphi team. Unsuccessful in more sympathetic roles, as far as villains were concerned he was said to be the best in the business. Abingdon was thin and dark with a mouth which curved down at the corners giving him a sardonic air. Jessie, for some reason she could not explain, found it hard to like him, but recognised his worth in the company. Will, always less critical, was simply amused by his often boastful behaviour.

One evening the Stage Doorkeeper handed Will a letter by mistake and without looking at it closely, Will opened it. Seeing then that it was addressed to Abingdon he went to find him and apologise but Abingdon had not yet arrived.

"It's not torn," said Jessie. "Seal it up and send it back down again. He'll never know."

"Luckily it was only a bill from his bootmaker," said Will. "He can be a touchy fellow."

Later that evening Billy Abingdon came into Will's dressing room carrying the very letter. He opened it ostentatiously, read it with a superior smile and then tore it into pieces, saying, "Another silly little fool of a married woman who wants me to take her out to supper." He was startled and none too pleased when Will roared with laughter.

Abingdon's taste in females was exotic and it was at this time that he made the acquaintance of a 'Mrs Maggie Archer' who plied her trade on the notorious Empire Promenade. This particular 'Promenade' was at the back of the dress circle of the famous Music Hall, the Empire, Leicester Square; and here the more flamboyant prostitutes would stroll. This traffic outraged the delightfully named Mrs Ormiston Chant, and her Purity Party, dubbed by the now ageing critic, Clement Scott, 'Prudes on the Prowl'. After continued protest they succeeded in having a trellis erected, backed with canvas, to screen the women from view. A young cadet from Sandhurst, called Winston Churchill, was among the three hundred young men who, one night, pulled the barrier down. On November 5 1894, Mrs Chant's effigy replaced Guy Fawkes, and on the Promenade it was 'business as usual'.

By a strange and ultimately fateful coincidence, Abingdon's latest fancy, Maggie Archer, was the half-sister of the deluded actor, Richard Archer. Since his original engagement as a supernumerary in *Harbour Lights*, far from becoming the leading player that he felt his talent deserved, he had found it increasingly difficult to obtain work of any kind in the theatre, and had returned to Scotland. At one time he was reduced to becoming a valet to a Guards Officer, and it was after this episode that, on returning to the stage, he augmented his name to Richard Archer Prince, adding for touring purpose, 'late Adelphi Theatre.' His unstable character and his delusion of being a 'great – albeit unrecognised actor' estranged him from his more pragmatic colleagues.

Even when he was without employment, he would still haunt the theatre, making a nuisance of himself in the audience, and often threatening the actors. He accused agents of preventing him from working and, when once more, 'Mad Archer' left to try his luck in London, many citizens of his native Dundee could not have been more delighted. And so it was that Richard Archer Prince got in touch again with his half-sister Maggie and through her acquaintance with Abingdon, obtained a walk on part at the Adelphi in *One of the Best*.

Halfway through the run, territorial disputes in the Sudan erupted between France and England, and Will Terriss decided that an extra, topical speech, inserted into the script might be just the thing. Seymour duly obliged and, as he was himself playing at the Gaiety that night, he sent Ellaline to report. After the show he sat at a table in the Gatti's Adelaide Gallery restaurant, sipping a glass of the wonderful cognac, bought cheaply during the Franco-Prussian war, and now sold at a modest profit, for which the restaurant was justly famous.

The Adelaide Gallery had two entrances. The one in Adelaide Street itself was mostly used by less affluent clients. Seated at small, marble- topped tables near the door could be found foreign customers enjoying dishes piled high with macaroni. The curving entrance from the Strand was a grander affair with steps leading up into the long gallery itself. The table nearest the kitchen and between the two areas was, as always, occupied by the two Gatti brothers, Agostino and Stephano, from where they could supervise every dish.

"Darling!" Ellaline, wearing a long, pale grey velvet coat and a small hat covered with irridescent blue feathers, hurried in to join her husband. "I'm sorry I've been so long," she said kissing him. "I met Maudie and I couldn't get away. Good house?"

"Packed," said Seymour, settling her chair. "But a bit slow on the uptake."

"Oh, bad luck." Ellaine peeled off her gloves.

"Well ... " said Seymour, eagerly, "how was it then? Did he remember it all?"

Ellaline laughed. "I wish you could have been there. It was quite incredible. Pa started off ... you know ... just as you wrote it ... *A hundred years ago, the guns of Europe* etc ... but, after a few more words ... I'm afraid he completely lost it ... "

"Oh Lord," said Seymour, putting his head in his hands. "I knew it!"

At that moment there was a commotion as Will Terriss

hurried in, saluted the proprietors, and greeted various aquaintances.

"Seymour, dear boy," he said sitting down beside them and kissing Ellaline.

"Just a few alterations, I think – but I was right! It was splendid. Got a huge response didn't it, Ellie?"

Ellaline burst into laughter. "Father! You are completely shameless."

Will looked affronted. "What do you mean? It brought the house down."

"Of course it did but ... it wasn't what Seymour wrote," she chided.

"It was cutting it a bit fine, sir," said Seymour. "A new speech – half an hour before curtain up."

"My dear boy, " said Will, signalling to the waiter. "There's nothing an audience likes better than a topical reference. This new row with the French .... it's much too good. to miss. Thank you, George. Champagne, Ellie? Ah! that's very good! Now, don't worry, Seymour, old chap.. I'll have it by tomorrow night."

Seymour's eye was at that moment distracted by Abingdon who, with Maggie on his arm, had just come through the door. She wore a red and black striped dress cut so low it barely covered her nipples. Black ostrich plumes caught together with a diamante buckle decorated her wide-brimmed hat.

"Och, what will you think of next, Billy?" she said, ogling the room defiantly, her voice husky, her Scottish accent exaggerated. As they passed Seymour's table Abingdon bowed.

"Good evening Miss Terriss, Mr Terriss, Mr Hicks," he intoned ingratiatingly. "Rather warm for the time of year is it not?"

"Yes, it is," said Will, amused, but open and friendly." Very warm."

As Abingdon led Maggie Archer past them to a table in the corner, there was an overpowering scent of carnations.

"Good Lord!" said Seymour. "Where did she come from?"

"I've no idea," said Will. "She's his latest feature backstage, I gather."

Seymour shook his head. "How does he do it?"

"Fatal charm, old chap ." answered Will. "They do say she 'walks on' at the Empire and is Archer Prince's sister. Rather more successful than her brother by the look of it."

"Who's Archer Prince?" asked Ellaline.

"Oh, just one of the supers," said Will. "He's been walking on for years I think. Strange, unfortunate fellow. I believe they call him 'Mad Archer' "

"Is he mad?" asked Seymour.

Will shook his head." Just a bit eccentric, I think," he answered, completely unaware that the spur which Archer Prince's dormant madness needed was almost at hand, and that the actor's general, smouldering resentment would soon be fatally focussed.

"Well, his sister's certainly an eyeful!" said Seymour.

"Seymour!" cried Ellaline, mock scandalised.

"Sorry darling," Seymour said, "but ... well ... just look at her."

"Jess has never really liked Abingdon, " said Will.

"The old Adelphi wouldn't be the same without him," said Seymour.

"Absolutely right, my boy," Will agreed, sipping his champagne. "Oh, excuse me a moment. There's old Slark. He's only just out of hospital. I must see how he is."

Terriss dashed across the room to greet a pale, elderly gentleman, leaning heavily on a stick, while Seymour smoothed the crumpled script he'd left behind.

"I'm not sure that having one's Pa-in-law starring in one's play is such a brilliant idea after all," he mused.

"Seymour! How could you?" Ellaline pouted.

"Darling, you know I don't mean it. I'm eternally grateful to him but ... well ... if he's going to want a re-write every other night ... " he sighed. "Did he remember any of it?"

"Oh yes," said Ellaline brightly. "And of course, even after he got lost he just made it up. No-one would have known."

"Thanks so much," Seymour's shoulders drooped.

"Oh darling. I mean ... he didn't let you down. He said something about 'Our beloved Queen ... '"

"That always gets them going..."

"Yes," smiled Ellaline, "and then he remembered 'Great Britain feared no Frenchman then, she fears no Frenchman now...' and the whole audience just stood up and cheered."

"I don't think he needs my words at all, " said Seymour. "He's so popular he could get a round of applause just reciting the train time-table."

"And then, " laughed Ellaline, "he looked up at my box and gave me the most enormous wink!"

Will Terriss rejoined them, and beckoning to the waiter, asked "Now ... what shall we have? Salmon and strawberries and down to work, eh?"

From their table across the room, Abingdon and Maggie watched.

"God knows what they're changing now," said Abingdon, scornfully. "Tonight – if you please – we were treated to a completely new version of his speech in Act Two. Typical Terriss! The audience were bewildered. They could make no sense of it at all. And who could blame them? The man is arrogance personified."

Maggie sipped her drink and regarded Terriss with veiled interest. "Indeed," she said softly.

Abingdon's face hardened. "He wouldn't dare take such liberties with everyone's work, but ... when you have the author in your pocket. well ... " he sneered, " ... nepotism is king."

"Just so, Billy, " said Maggie, stroking his arm.

"No respect for other actors, of course," continued Abingdon, bitterly. "But then," he scoffed, "there's nothing to playing the hero. Anyone could do it."

"Is that so?" Maggie was relieved when the waiter brought the oysters.

"My dear girl," said Abingdon, letting the first one glide down his throat. "The parts are superficial." He took another. "Foolproof! A child could play them."

Maggie watched him as he deftly twisted a third oyster out of the shell and swallowed it. Billy Abingdon was her best catch yet, and she was going to hang on to him!

"I'm sure you're right, Billy," she smiled and circled her lips with her tongue.

"Audiences just don't understand that when they cheer the hero," continued Abingdon. "Now – to portray the villain – ah, that, my dear Maggie, takes acting of real quality." He threw back his head and swallowed the last oyster. "One needs finesse," he said, wiping his mouth delicately. "Timing, and a power far beyond the talents of ... " he indicated Terriss ... "a certain gentleman. As I explained to your brother the other evening."

"I'm not sure you should encourage Archer," said Maggie, suddenly concerned. She pushed away her plate. "He's not quite ..." she looked embarrassed. "Well ... he takes things oddly and ... this rehearsal you're planning ... I'm not so sure it's at all a good idea."

"Nonsense," said Abingdon, taking her hand and nibbling it. "Why shouldn't he have a chance? It's just a little harmless fun, my dear." His strong teeth closed over her tingling fingers. "And you like a little fun, don't you Maggie?"

It was late afternoon the next day. Back-stage at the Adelphi, two supers in the cast of *One of the Best* were joined by a third. Cathcart was a short, tubby man, perpetually out of breath.

"What's all this about then, Simkins? " he puffed, hurrying in.

Simkins, a pale, weasel-faced individual, tipped back his chair and shrugged. "'Pon my soul, I'm not sure."

Murray, the third man, who was walking idly up and down,

picked up a drum from the prop table and tapped it softly with his fingers. His face, with its heavy jaw, was pockmarked.

"Abingdon's having some sort of jape with old Archer." he growled. "Letting him run through Terriss's part."

"Mad Archer?" said Cathcart. "You can't be serious? I ... I thought it was a proper rehearsal."

"So did I," said Simkins, straightening his chair. "What's Abingdon up to then?"

"Who knows,?" answered Murray. "Sir Abingdon is a law unto himself, is he not?

"I can't say I like the fellow ..." began Simkins.

"Nor I, my dear old chap," agreed Cathcart.

"An odd sense of humour ... but ... all those years of playing the villain." Simkins shook his head. "Just imagine it. Everyone hating   you ... "

"And never getting the girl .... "

"He certainly makes up for that, off-stage," sneered Murray.

"Well ... it doesn't do to upset him, dear," said Cathcart. "He can always put in a word for you in the right quarter."

"True, oh, Queen, said Murray. "He did mention a certain something. I think he's just pleasing his wench ... she is Archer's sister after all."

"I wouldn't mind pleasing her myself," grinned Simkins, wolfishly."

"Simkins, old chap," exclaimed Cathcart, rolling his eyes. "As I never cease telling you, you have appalling taste."

"Sh," said Murray quietly, "here they come. My God! Will you look at Archer."

Archer Prince strode onto the stage. He was tall and thin. He had a heavy moustache and his pronounced, black eyebrows emphasised a slight cast in one eye. He bowed solemnly to the three other supers. He carried a script, a sword and had a plaid draped across his shoulders. His eyes glittered and his angular body was tense with excitement. Abingdon followed with Maggie, slightly tipsy, holding onto his arm.

"Ah, Cathcart, Simkins, and Murray too. How good of you to help us," he said to the bemused supers, who, nevertheless, sensed some sport to come.

"I wish Mr Prince here," he said, "to have his chance to run through some of the role of Lieutenant Keppel of the Scottish Highlanders."

Archer Prince gave another exaggerated bow. The supers hid their smiles.

"A role for which," continued Abingdon, loftily, "coming, as he does, from Dundee, he is – as I am sure you will agree – perfectly suited."

At this Archer Prince began to parade around the stage. Abingdon smiled. "One day who knows," he said solemnly, "he may yet have the opportunity to play the role."

Cathcart and Simkins exchanged glances, Murray could not take his eyes off Archer Prince.

"We'll begin with the trial scene," said Abingdon, rubbing his hands. "Cathcart, do you think you could manage the Sergeant?"

"No problem at all," said Cathcart eagerly. He crossed to where Archer now stood to attention and gripped his arm dramatically.

"Good," said Abingdon. "I myself will read the General. And the others must fill in all the noises from the crowd. Now ... we need a drummer. Just a steady beat will do. Maggie dear, take the drum and play us in, won't you."

Maggie Archer sauntered over to the prop table where Murray had replaced the drum, all eyes but her brother's upon her. As she began a slow, insistent beat, Archer Prince and Cathcart marched centre stage.

"*Halt!*" shouted Cathcart.

Abingdon, clearly relishing playing the General, drew himself up and stood before Archer Prince.

"*Officers and men of the second highlanders,*" he began in a loud voice.

"You have been summoned here today to hear Her Majesty's sentence on one who I am ashamed to say has stained his Queen's commission with treachery. Lieutenant Keppel. Fall out!"

Archer Prince stepped forward.

"I am here, Sir," he said simply, in a strong Scottish brogue.

Murray and Simkins booed and hissed loudly and were rewarded with a lofty smile from Abingdon who continued ...

"Silence! Lieutenant Keppel. I address you by your title for the last time. You have been found guilty of the most terrible crime that a soldier can be accused of in times of peace ... You have endeavoured to betray your country to a foreign power."

Archer Prince started forward, his arm raised as if to protest, then fell back again and hung his head. His movements were mechanical and clearly much rehearsed.

Abingdon took a deep breath.

"You have been convicted. You have dragged through the mire the cloth which our comrades who have gone before dyed scarlet with their blood on the fields of the Peninsula and the plain of Waterloo. The sentence of this court is that you be stripped of all titles and that you be drummed out of the service and sent to penal servitude for the term of your natural life ... "

"A little faster on the drum now, Maggie," he called.

Maggie, her eyes excited, began a rapid tattoo.

"Sergeant," commanded Abingdon, *"Do your duty."*

With a broad smile Cathcart advanced upon Archer Prince who threw up his arm.

"Stop!" he cried. *"Before this terrible sentence is carried out, I swear as there is a God above me that I am innocent of this awful charge. Some day when it is too late – you will know*

that I – Dudley Keppel – never disgraced the country I served,
or the uniform I wear."

Murray and Simkins closed in upon the scene menacingly, and hissed.

"Sergeant! Your duty!" repeated Abingdon.

Cathcart and the other Supers mimed stripping Archer Prince of his collar and cuffs. They pulled at his clothes. They were rough and enjoyed it.

"Now his sword. Now his medals"

Abingdon too caught the mood. *"Unfold your arms!"* he yelled.

"Stay," cried Archer. *"You may take my name… my honour and my life … but you cannot take my Victoria Cross."*

Archer Prince paused and surveyed them all, and there was a subtle shift in the balance of power in the scene.

"Now I am ready," he said. *"God save the Queen!"*

"Excellent, Archer," said Abingdon grandiosely. "My word, you've got it just right. Now we'll cut to the final scene."

Archer Prince looked crestfallen. "But … but the speech in the cell, Mr Abingdon, " he cried." I've learned it."

"Yes, Archer, but I hardly think we have time … "

"Oh please, Abingdon … " Archer Prince pleaded. "Sir, just the last bit …" he began a frantic pacing.

"The last time I shall ever hear the hour told in England," he cried. *"Oh my God! How terrible! Is there no way? Is there no chance?"* He became increasingly distraught. His voice rose.

"The walls seem to close in and stifle me. The last night! It can't be … I shall go mad!"

Suddenly he became rigid. His eyes seemed to bulge, then he threw out his arms and screamed.

"I SHALL GO MAD!"

Maggie stopped drumming. Abingdon looked uneasy.

"Very good, Archer, he said "Er ... most convincing."

"Christ! He'll be foaming at the mouth next," murmured Murray to Simkins.

"Right," said Abingdon hastily. "Now to the last scene where Keppel is found innocent and pardoned." He – took out his watch. "We'll cut my first speech. I'll go from:

"In the presence of your regiment we proclaim your innocence."

The supers cheered, automatically.

"Lieutenant Keppel," continued Abingdon, *"as some compensation."*

Archer Prince seemed calmer as he cut in ...

"Compensation? General I ask for none, but to have once more the trust and esteem of my General, the affection of my men and the commission of my Queen."

There was a pause. The supers looked blankly at one another. The fun, it seemed, was over.

"Very good, Archer." said Abingdon relieved. "Maggie dear, wasn't that good?"

But Maggie did not answer, her eyes were half-shut. "Ah, my dear fellow," Abingdon put an arm around Archer. "if only the world might see your rendering, there is no doubt it would put others in the shade."

While Archer preened, Murray noted the venom with which Abingdon spoke and smiled to himself.

"He can't be comparing him with Terriss?" whispered Cathcart.

"Who else," Simkins raised an eyebrow and shuddered.

Archer bowed. "Thank you, Sir." His face glowed with pleasure.

"Not at all," Abingdon, amused, returned the bow. "It is merely your due. If only you had a chance to play it ... but ...

one never knows. My dear Archer … in the theatre nothing is impossible and so … let us continue. Cathcart, have you got the sword?"

"Lieutenant Keppel," Abingdon intoned. *"The compensation I speak of comes from the Queen. We hand back your sword."*

Cathcart handed the sword to Archer who took it ceremoniously and very slowly ran his finger down the blade.

"You are a true soldier whose patriotism is beyond all doubt, whose heart is strong in the day of battle," concluded Abingdon with a satisfied smirk. The fun was over.

But suddenly Archer Prince lifted his sword high above his head.
"My sword is sacred," he began softly, menacingly. Then his voice rose.

"Instinct with the glorious memories of Inkerman and Balaclava, of Lucknow and Cawnpore …"

now exultantly he spoke to the sword, his eyes ablaze …
"BAPTISED WITH THE BLOOD OF HEROES!"

There was a moment of stunned silence. The figure of fun had become suddenly unpredictable, alarming. Abingdon coughed.
"Yes, Archer. No doubt about it. Marvellous. Splendid. Thank you, gentlemen one and all for your cooperation. Maggie dear … He moved away. The little group broke up. Only Archer Prince stood as if in a trance.
"Bloody terrifying, if you ask me," muttered Murray.
"There'll be no stopping him now," said Cathcart. "We'll never hear the last of it."

The supers left in an odd, uncomfortable silence.

Only Maggie looked back at Archer. His arm had dropped. He carefully laid the sword in its place on the table. He paced around the stage as if his feet were very light. He held his head a little to one side. Their eyes met. He smiled grandly. He seemed dazed, exalted. Maggie stared, shrugged and left.

Half an hour later Archer Prince let himself into his lodgings and climbed the narrow, dingy staircase to the attic. His room was small, the bed unmade and littered with papers. Lying down amongst them he stared at the ceiling and slowly his dreams of the gallant Highland Officer playing to a cheering audience faded. Replaced as they were by the grim reality of his surroundings, mounting resentment made him grind his teeth in an impotent rage.

CHAPTER THIRTEEN

"Why couldn't the fellow have just sent it round?" Will Terriss asked, drumming his fingers on the arm of the chair. It was November of the following year.

One of the Best, after a good run of seven months, had been replaced by another military melodrama set in Egypt and the Sudan, and called *Boys Together*; but already the quest to find the next play had begun.

"I should never have let you persuade me," he continued.

"Oh, Will," sighed Jessie, "he wrote a really charming letter and Ellen thinks it's the finest piece he's ever written. She's sure it's a wonderful part for you."

"But ... you know I simply hate having plays read to me, Jess," he protested.

Jessie had moved from Shaftesbury Avenue to a more elegant and spacious flat in Princes Street, near Hanover Square. On the dark red walls of the drawing room hung many signed photgraphs, including those of Irving and Ellen Terry.

Jessie, wearing a deep blue velvet dress with bands of flowered ribbon stitched around the cuffs and hem, sat looking out of the long window. Will lounged by the fire in an armchair.

"There's a most peculiar person to see you," announced Lottie, putting her head round the door. "Says he's a playwright. Looks more like a farmer to me."

Jessie rose, smiling. "It's all right Lottie, it's Mr Shaw. We're expecting him. Show him up, will you?"

"If you say so," said Lottie, clearly not convinced.

"Dearest Will," begged Jessie. "Do try to look a little more enthusiastic."

Will sighed but as George Bernard Shaw strode purposefully into the room, a bulky parcel under his arm, he rose to greet him with his usual charm.

"Shaw, my dear fellow," he said. "Good of you to come. Can I get you anything?"

"Nothing, thank you." Shaw, clearly disinterested in social niceties, sat down on the nearest chair, crossed his long legs, encased in knickerbockers and heavy knitted stockings, and unwrapped his manuscript. Will, taken somewhat aback, sat down again by the fire and Jessie took the chair next to Shaw.

"'The Devil's Disciple', a melodrama," began Shaw, without more ado.

"At the most wretched hour between a black night and a wintry morning in 1777," he began solemnly, "Mrs Dudgeon, of New Hampshire, is sitting in the kitchen and general dwellingroom of her farmhouse on the outskirts of Websterbridge. She is not a prepossessing woman... "

As the reading continued it was already clear that Will did not consider Shaw either a particularly prepossessing author, much less a reader.

"No woman looks her best after sitting up all night..." continued Shaw.

Jessie, seeing Will's totally puzzled face, tried hard to control a giggle. Would Shaw ever get into the play itself?

However, when at last he did, each character sounded exactly the same. On and on he droned, his strong Irish brogue having an almost hypnotic effect. To her horror Jessie saw Will's eyes closing. As Shaw paused for breath she interrupted.

"Will, my dear, could we change seats? I'm feeling a little chilly."

Will came to with a start. "What? Of course, my dear. You should have said so before," he added, embarrassed, as they changed places. Shaw gave Terriss a sharp look and continued at once.

"Would such a selfish wretch as Peter have come thirty miles to see Timothy hanged?" he intoned. *"Not thirty yards, not he!"*

Jessie stole a glance at Shaw as he read. He was as unaware of the monotony of his reading as he was enthralled with his lengthy script. She smiled to herself, thinking back to Irving's wonderful readings at the Lyceum. What would he have made of this? The expressionless voice continued. By now she, too, was feeling drowsy and could no longer sort out the characters or the plot.

"No," said Shaw, *"Richard has saved him, he has gone to save himself. Richard must die."*

Will, she saw, was now asleep. She hoped he wouldn't snore. Suddenly Shaw stopped. Will, woken by the sudden silence, leapt to his feet.

"Thank you, Shaw, " he said. "But...I'm afraid it won't do. The ending is wrong for the Adelphi you see ...."

Shaw's face flushed with anger. He rose to his feet. "That was not the end of the play," he thundered. "It was but the end of Act Two, Mr Terriss. But I shall not go on. I shall take my leave at once."

"Oh," cried Jessie. "Surely not without some refreshment, Mr Shaw?"

"Of course, good idea," said Will, hurriedly. "You must be dry, Shaw. Whisky and soda, old chap?"

Shaw backed away as if he had been struck in the face. "I never drink anything but water, sir!" he exploded.

It was Will's turn to look astonished.

"Heavens!" said Jessie, desperately." It's almost four o'clock. I was so engrossed in your play, Mr Shaw I had no idea of the time. We dine in twenty minutes. Won't you join us? I know Cook is preparing a delicious saddle of lamb."

An expression of the utmost horror spread across Shaw's

face. He picked up his manuscript and strode to the door. He turned. "I never touch meat of any sort," his voice shook with rage. "Good day!."

Will and Jessie stood for a moment looking at the door which slammed behind him, before falling into each other's arms. When at last Jessie could control her laughter, she wiped her eyes. "Poor Mr Shaw," she gasped.

"Poor Mr Shaw indeed?" said Will. "I was never so bored in all my life."

"I'm afraid that was only too obvious," said Jessie.

Will kissed her hands. "Lord, Jess, "he said," that voice ... just going on and on."

"But you didn't hear the half of it," protested Jessie. "You were… "

"Rubbish! Just had my eyes closed," grinned Will.

"Oh, my dear, he'll never forgive you..." Jessie shook her head.

"Can't be helped," said Will.

"And then you offered him a whisky and soda!"

"How was I to know he drinks nothing but water?" said Will, sitting down. "No wonder he writes such damned dull plays – and such terrible titles! *The Devil's Disciple!* I ask you? Anyway," he laughed. "you didn't make things much better by asking him to stay to dinner."

"Ellen might have warned me he was a vegetarian," said Jessie.

"Thoroughly peculiar chap, if you ask me." said Will, poking the fire. "Supposed to be clever but, he's certainly no judge of our audiences." He turned and looked at her, his blue eyes alight with amusement. Remember what he called poor Seymour's *One of the Best?*"

Jessie laughed. "Yes. *One of the Worst!*. And he said it wouldn't run."

"Exactly," said Will, picking up the paper and opening it. "Man's an idiot. Jess, I can't stay to eat."

"Oh Will … " Jessie looked disappointed. He always seemed so busy lately. He had so many interests apart from the theatre. Recently, to everyone's surprise, he had bought a licensed premises in Covent Garden. His friends all trooped down to see the new proprietor's name put up over the door but be used the family name and William Charles Lewin was displayed.

"How is the Market House doing?" asked Jessie.

"Very nicely, as it happens," said Will with a grin. "But I've found I have to keep a gin bottle filled with water behind the bar."

"Whatever for?"

"There's always someone who insists on being served by the proprietor and buying him a drink," laughed Will. "I'm sorry, I can't stay, darling girl, but I have to meet old Graves. Could you ring for some tea?"

"I'll get Lottie to do it," said Jessie. "Cook will be busy." Jessie rang for Lottie.

"Your visitor, Mr Shaw, left in a high old temper," observed Lottie, as she came in. "Someone upset his apple cart and no mistake."

"Oh dear," said Jessie ruefully. "Never mind. Lottie, could we have some tea please?. Mr Terriss has to leave directly."

"I'll see to it straight away, " said Lottie. Jessie moved a small pile of books from the table to make way for the tea, then came to look over Will's shoulder. She slid her arms down his chest. How warm and solid he was and how she loved him still. She just wished that they could spend more time together. Perhaps one day …. Her thoughts were interrupted by Lottie who returned with the tea tray.

"Thank you, Lottie. Put it there, will you?" Jessie sat and poured.

"Good Lord!," exclaimed Will, suddenly looking at his watch. "Is that the time? I must fly."

"But your tea?" said Jessie.

"Drink it for me, my dearest love," said Will, already at the door. "I've got to tie up the ends of the tour and then … " he grinned. "There's a distinct possibility of Australia."

"Australia?" cried Jessie. "That's the first I've heard about it."

"Nothing definite yet," said Will. "But it sounds promising – they'd want a bit of Shakespeare and some minor classics- make a change, wouldn't it?"

"Wonderful," said Jessie.

"And we might even do a spell in South Africa on the way home – we'll talk about it later." He dashed across the room, and kissed her firmly on the mouth.

He traced her eyebrows with his finger, gently pressed her nose with his thumb, grinned and ran back to the door. "I'll see you in the theatre," he called, and was gone.

Jessie sipped her tea abstractedly. It was as if he took some of the brightness out of her life when he left. He was always busy, always making plans. She wished …. in fact … she didn't know what she wished. She sighed and rang for Lottie.

"I thought it was Mr Terriss wanted the tea," said Lottie.

"It was," sighed Jessie, "and then he was in too much of a hurry to drink it."

Lottie shrugged. "Not the first time – nor will it be the last. Have you finished, Miss Jessie?"

"Yes, thank you. No … I might have another cup."

Lottie raised her eyebrows and waited.

'Oh, clear it away," said Jessie. "I don't want any more. "

Lottie loaded the tray and as she lifted it she caught her foot in the rug and stumbled for a moment, rattling the cups.

"Oh heavens," Jessie's voice was sharp. "You are so clumsy!"

Lottie, clearly upset, looked at her mistress.

"I'm very sorry," she said quietly.

"Oh, Lottie, forgive me, I didn't mean it," said Jessie. "You know I didn't mean it."

Lottie stood her ground. "I daresay I am clumsy sometimes, Miss" she said in a flat voice. "I'm sure I'm very sorry."

Jessie jumped to her feet. "Oh, don't look at me like that," she said. "I don't know what's the matter with me lately. I feel … all on edge somehow. Do you think it can be the weather?"

"I'm sure I couldn't say. " Lottie was unyielding.

"Oh, don't be cross with me," cried Jessie. "I can't bear it. Leave the wretched tray and stay upstairs with me. I don't want to be alone."

Lottie's face softened. "I'll take the tray," she said, "and fetch my mending."

Jessie crossed to the ornate mirror which hung over the mantelpiece. She looked at herself, at the faint but visible frown lines between her eyebrows. Her face had grown fuller, the clear outlines just a shade blurred. She turned her head sideways and smoothed her neck.

"Oh I do wish I was beautiful," she said, as Lottie returned.

Lottie sat down and lifted the lid of her sewing box. "Well, Miss Jessie," she said, matter-of-factly, "You do your very best. You use everything there is."

"Oh, Lottie!" Jessie laughed. "What would I do without you?"

Lottie smiled, threaded her needle and began to darn. "How was Miss Terry when you called?" she asked.

"Oh, much better," answered Jessie, sitting down again. "It was really only a chill." She paused. "She had both her grandchildren with her."

"That was nice for her," said Lottie, carefully pulling the woollen thread.

"Yes," said Jessie. "The baby was asleep in his pram and little Rosie – she's two and a half now – I wish you could have seen her. Ellen calls her her sunbeam. She says she wishes there could be another baby every year."

Lottie sniffed. "All right for her," she said. "She can send them home when she gets tired of them."

"I suppose so," said Jessie. "Rosie looked up at me with her great blue eyes, Lottie, and put her fat little hand on my knee and I suddenly felt … I don't know. Jealous I suppose." Jessie stood up and walked across to the fire. She looked down into the glowing coals. "She has it all, Ellen. Doesn't she?" she said quietly. "She's a great actress ... and she's had husbands, children, and now grandchildren and I ... "

"You're broody," said Lottie, putting down her needle and looking at Jessie.

"I beg your pardon?" Jessie turned.

"Broody," repeated Lottie. "That's what you are. I should have thought of that."

"I don't understand ... "

"You being thirty-five last birthday," said Lottie.

"I hope you're not going round telling everyone I'm thirty-five," exclaimed Jessie.

Lottie smiled and shook her head. "My lips are sealed, " she said. "But that's what's wrong with you. Depend on it. My sister Lou was just the same. Thirty-five and impossible."

"What did she do?" asked Jessie, her eyes wide.

"Ran off with the man next door and came back with twins!" said Lottie. As Jessie laughed, the bell rang. "That's Cook," said Lottie getting to her feet.

"Your dinner's ready. Come on 'Miss Jessie' you get your mind back onto your work. You've got a performance tonight."

Lottie bustled out. As Jessie moved to follow her she once more crossed to the mirror. She paused, looking at her reflection in some surprise. But as she stood there her great dark eyes began to glisten with tears.

As the production of *Boys Together*, in which Abingdon had played a particularly odious villain, came to an end, the Gattis searched for a suitable play to follow it. Something which would provide good starring parts for their hero and heroine. As it would take them over the Christmas period of 1896 they eventually decided on a revival of a popular old nautical melodrama which took its title from John Gay's song about *Black Eyed Susan*.

Written in 1829 by Douglas Jerrold it was as authentic a nautical piece as possible since the author had himself been a midshipman under Nelson. There were lively characters, Doggrass. Gnatbrain, Quid, Pike, Hatchet and Seaweed.

The hero, another William, was the original Jolly Jack Tar and spoke a curious but vivid language of his own. Terriss had the sense to see that it should be played exactly as it was written.

On returning to port to meet his wife Susan. William declares.

"Huzza, my noble fellows. My heart jumps like a dolphin. My head turns round like a capstern. I feel as though I were driving before the gale of pleasure for the heaven of joy."

But when Susan is not there to meet him he describes his disappointment:

"My heart knocks against my timbers, like a jolly boat in a breeze alongside a seventy four. Damn it! I feel as though half of me was wintering in the Baltic and the other half stationed in Jamaica."

Terriss was probably the only actor of his day, or any other, capable of carrying this off and he did it brilliantly, even singing and dancing a hornpipe. The whole company entered into the spirit of the piece and the Adelphi audiences loved it.

During the run of *Black Eyed Susan*, Agostino Gatti suddenly died. The theatre closed on the Saturday, the day of the funeral, and Will realised that he possessed no formal clothes in which to attend; the casual, grey tweeds which he always wore being quite unsuitable. His many friends immediately rallied round. Seymour Hicks provided a superbly glossy topper. Arthur Cohen, one of the smartest dressed men in London, lent him a stylish frock coat, and Lottie did her best to sponge and press an old pair of evening dress trousers.

"How do I look?" asked Will.

"Quite splendid!" laughed Jessie. "You should dress up more often."

Will pulled a face. "But you really should have a black waistcoat," she added.

Suddenly she remembered the black silk scarf which William puts around his sweetheart's neck in the final scene of the play. It was quickly sent for, ironed, and pinned carefully by Lottie over Will's own waistcoat. The frock coat was tightly buttoned and, impeccably attired, off he went to the funeral. It was the only time his friends had ever seen him offstage in formal clothes, and he couldn't wait to change out of them. He and Jessie were invited to George Edwardes' house for the weekend. Jessie went to meet him at Paddington with his own comfortable tweeds in a suitcase. He did a quick change before the train departed and the borrowed finery was left with the stationmaster to be collected.

But Gatti's sudden death affected Will. For the first time he began to consider his own mortality. He had just reached his fiftieth birthday although no-one would have suspected it. He thought about Jessie's position should he, too, have a sudden heart attack. She was an immensely popular actress and would, he considered, have no trouble finding work, but he knew how much she loved their home near Windsor. Without telling her, he resolved to add a codicil to his will, leaving her Jessamine Cottage and this he did, some weeks later.

CHAPTER FOURTEEN

Black Eyed Susan ended its run in March '97 and once again the hunt was on for a replacement production. None being immediately forthcoming, Stephano Gatti, rather than have the Adelphi dark, agreed to lease the theatre to an American company led by the actor William Gillette, who would star in his own play *Secret Service*. Will's contract at £55 per week, which included all costumes, save modern dress, and special billing in the *Daily Telegraph*, had already been renewed until '99. He was temporarily released and was snapped up by the management at the Haymarket to play in a comedy called *A Marriage of Convenience*.

Unfortunately there was no part for Jessie, the heroine being a seventeen year old convent schoolgirl. This did not please their many fans, and the play did not have a long run, but Jessie felt that 'resting' for a while might be beneficial.

It was a good moment to be on holiday. London was in buoyant mood. Queen Victoria celebrated her Diamond Jubilee that summer and the grand spectacle at St Paul's Cathedral was echoed by street parties all over the capital. Jessie took her mother and younger sister Flo, to the Victorian Era Exhibition at Earls Court. Open from 11am to 11pm it celebrated sixty years of British Art, History, Drama and Music, British women's work, Science, Sport and Picturesque England.

Jessie's mother was particularly interested in the pictures and Jubilee gifts which the Queen had graciously lent for display, and Jessie and her sister marvelled at the Gigantic Wheel. On another occasion they went to the Crystal Palace where there was a Jubilee Show of roses and stayed for the fireworks by Mr Brock. From such a vantage point high above London the effects were spectacular and advertised as being able to be witnessed by tens of thousands.

The beginning of that summer was not enjoyable for Richard Archer Prince. All contacts for work as a 'super' in London having failed, he had returned in desperation to his native city of Dundee. Shunned by the theatre, he eventually obtained a job in a foundry. During the day, the hard and monotonous labour seemed to calm him, but at weekends he would drink, becoming rowdy and extravagant, and his dreams were filled with the memories of his triumphant rehearsal at the Adelphi and the injustices he felt he had since suffered.

By an unfortunate chance a small northern company touring one of the past Adelphi melodramas called *The Union Jack*, suddenly found themselves on arrival in Glasgow without a villain. Archer Prince, 'late Adelphi', was cast. All his theatrical delusions were rekindled as the humble foundry worker was in an instant transformed into the elegant Sir Philip Yorke. The part contained a particularly gruesome stabbing in the final scene, and Prince played it in such a demented fashion, often forgetting his lines and moves, that by October the management had had enough and he was dismissed.

Yet within weeks of this episode he obtained another engagement. A Mr Croydon of Newcastle who ran a small company playing 'one night stands' and had clearly not heard of his reputation, signed him up for two plays. The roles of Sir Lester Lightfoot and Sir Geoffrey Dashwood, were both small but aristocratic. Once again it was his past association with the Adelphi in London that did the trick. Archer Prince's madness however, was becoming worse. Increasingly difficult and unpredictable at rehearsals, it was soon clear that he could not learn his lines and Mr Croydon was forced to sack him before the opening night. Archer Prince pleaded but was refused.

"Now I have two enemies!," he shouted. "One here and the other at the Adelphi."

"Who do you mean?" asked Croydon, a plump and amiable man who felt sorry for Prince but wished heartily that he had never set eyes on him.

Prince turned away. "Terriss," he muttered,

"Terriss!. William Terriss?" cried Mr Croydon. "You are ridiculous. Everyone holds Mr Terriss in the highest respect. He is a splendid actor."

Prince looked at him disdainfully and laughed. "Fools often succeed where men of genius fail," he declaimed, then turned abruptly and scuttled off. The following day he called at the theatre several times, begging for his wages. Croydon lost patience.

"I owe you nothing," he shouted exasperatedly. "Go away you madman!"

Prince glared at him, raised his fist, but then fell back. "Mad?" he said harshly. "Mad, am I? You will hear of my madness. The whole world will ring with it!"

He returned to his lodgings, packed his belongings, and set out for the docks to work his passage south. After an Indian summer, chill winds reminded people that it would soon be winter. By October, Archer Prince had reached London and found a room at three shillings a week in Buckingham Palace Road. His landlady, Mrs Darby, thought him quiet and gentlemanly, but noticed that his clothes were very shabby. The cutler who sold him a knife for 9d, he could not afford a better costing a shilling, also noted how poorly he was dressed.

At the Adelphi, Will and Jessie had taken over the leading roles in *Secret Service* when the American cast had gone, and it was to run over the Christmas period. Neither of them was particularly enthusiastic about the play, but it was work, they were playing together again and they were looking forward to the proposed tour. One night in early November they were discussing plans when a note was delivered to Will in his dressing room.

"Oh, Lord!" he exclaimed, on opening it. "This chap is becoming a nuisance."

"What is it?" asked Jessie.

"It's Archer Prince," said Terriss. "He's back in London and broke, poor fellow."

"That weird man who used to walk on?" asked Jessie. "The one with the squint?"

Will nodded and took a sheet of writing paper from his dressing table drawer.

"Have you got an envelope?" he asked. When Jessie returned with the envelope she looked over Will's shoulder. '*I have known the bearer R.A Prince as a hard-working actor,*' she read. "Isn't that overstating it a little?" she queried.

Will sighed. "Well it's no good writing 'he's a very odd, unfortunate fellow' is it? The poor devil has to eat, Jess. That's exactly what the Actors' Benevolent Fund is for."

"I suppose you're right," said Jessie, kissing the top of his head. "He gives me the shivers somehow."

"If he'd ever had a chance, who knows," said Will, sealing the envelope. "Anyway, I must do what I can."

Terriss's letter enabled Archer Prince to gain a few payments, but the benevolence of the fund was sorely tried by his repeated demands, and his long, often incoherent, letters describing his pitiful situation. At the end of November he once again paced up and down outside the office. The door opened and a new young clerk stuck his head out. "Name o' Prince?" he called.

"That is my name, young man," said Prince grandly, eyeing him up and down. The freckled youth handed him an envelope and cleared his throat.

"I'm requested to inform you, Mr Prince," he recited, "that this will be your last payment for a while, sir. In spite of recommendations, sir – the fund 'as to be administered fairly. I'm sure you understand that, sir." This speech delivered he bolted inside the office and shut the door. Prince tore open the envelope, pocketed the ten shillings and strode away, his face dark with anger.

December began with personal sadness for Will Terriss. His beloved daughter Ellaline had, with Seymour Hicks, been full of joy at the impending birth of their first child. Jessie was excited, Will intrigued, yet stunned at the thought of becoming a grandfather, and Seymour rushed to his wife's side each night as soon as the curtain fell at the Gaiety. But the birth was long and difficult and the baby boy died within two days. Ellaine went to Eastbourne to recover but was told that she would never have another child.

On 3rd of December there was yet more sadness. The whole country was shocked to read of unprecedented storms at Margate, and the disastrous sinking of the lifeboat. The following afternoon Jessie and Will sat quietly in her drawing room, Will reading the account in the paper.

"This is a dreadful business," he said.

"Just imagine the desolation in the town," sighed Jessie. "Nine drowned out of a crew of thirteen."

"They were all brave fellows," said Will. "You know, Jess, lifeboat men are real life heroes." He got up and crossed to the fireplace. "I've sent a donation to the Telegraph suggesting a fund be set up for the families."

"Children with no fathers," said Jess. "And almost Christmas."

Will gazed into the fire. "I know what it's like to be in peril on the sea," he said quietly. "You cannot imagine the power of those great waves. I still remember our journey back from the Falklands all those years ago ... Isabel and Ella and Tom," he shook his head. "God help me, Tom as yet unborn. I must have been mad to risk their lives," his voice broke. He covered his eyes and Jessie realised that he was crying.

"My dear," she went swiftly to him. "What is it?"

"It's nothing."

Jessie insisted. "Will – you must tell me. Are you ill?"

Will shook his head and sat down. "No. No. It's Isabel." He looked up at her, his eyes brimming with tears. "Oh Jess. So many sorrows all at once. And now... Isabel is dying."

Jess knelt beside him. "Oh, my dear." Somehow it was a relief that at last he knew.

"I had lunch with Bob," said Will, wiping his eyes. "He says there's no hope. I went straight back to Bedford Park but she was asleep. I ... I didn't want to disturb her. I'll go back again after the theatre," he added almost apologetically.

"Of course," said Jessie gently.

Will looked at her. "You don't seem surprised."

Jessie coloured. "No. I've known for some time," she said. "Bob told me. That weekend he came down to the cottage."

"So long ago?" exclaimed Will. "Why wasn't I told?"

"She did not wish it."

"But why not?" The blue eyes were hurt and bewildered.

"You'll have to ask her," answered Jessie simply.

"I thought she looked more frail than usual last week," said Will, "but I imagined she was worrying about Ella. And I've been so busy with all the details and the contracts for the tour and now ... God forgive me. And you, Jess," he took her hands, "you've been on edge lately too. Was this the reason?"

"Perhaps ... partly," admitted Jessie.

"What a selfish brute I am," said Will crossing abruptly to look out of the window into the already darkening street. "Two women unhappy ... "

"Nonsense," said Jessie joining him. "Let's pull the curtains, I hate the fog. You mustn't reproach yourself," she added, leading him back to the fire. "It isn't your fault that Isabel is ill."

"I can't be sure of that," said Will. "All those early years – I dragged her half across the world and back – thoughtless, foolhardy young idiot that I was. All those crazy ventures that ended in failure."

"You were not to know that," said Jessie taking his hand. "And I'm sure she went willingly enough … "

"I should have been more responsible," cried Will.

"I don't suppose she saw it that way at all," reassured Jessie. "It must have seemed a wonderful adventure to be at your side," she added wistfully.

He smiled at her and pulled her close. He stroked her hair. "Perhaps you're right," he said. "Oh Jess. How simple life seems when one is young. It's only as we grow older that the edges blur and then … " He sighed. "Nothing is simple, is it?"

Jessie kissed him. "We must have faith in each other," she said. "And try to keep our lives as simple as we can."

"Dearest, dearest Jess." How much he loved her, so honest, so passionate, so much younger than him yet, in the fourteen years since they had first met, he had discovered her resilience. He couldn't imagine his life without her.

"Bob says Isabel may only have few months," he said. "The national tour's no problem – we can postpone it – but I … I can't think about Australia now …"

"Of course not," said Jessie. "They'll understand."

"I must be here … I must be with her as much as I can, until," he turned his head away then he took her hands and looked at her. "And then we'll go. We'll go to the other side of the world," he said fiercely. "Jess. Will you marry me in Australia?" he asked desperately.

"Oh my darling," said Jess. "It seems so awful …

"I know. But I need to hear you say it," he implored her.

Her heart leapt. "After all these years you doubt it?" She clung to him and hid her face.

"If we come back via South Africa we can do four months," said Will, "and after that – who knows. I'm getting tired of the melodrama. I'm too old to be in mortal danger at nine thirty every night and rescued in the nick of time at a quarter past ten."

Jessie laughed. "Your public won't let you go."

"They'll have no choice. I'll be forgotten in a week," said Will. "What d'you say, Jess? Shall we retire?" He grinned. "Better while I'm still in favour than linger on as a decrepit old gentleman."

Then his face changed." Oh, Jess, forgive me. You're young. You must continue – if you wish."

Jessie looked away. "I think there are all sorts of possibilities ... if I were to marry and leave the stage, " she said.

Will looked surprised. "Oh," he enquired, "what would you like to take up, Jess?"

Jessie blushed. "Well," she said " I'm not sure but ... what do most brides look forward to...?"

Will looked puzzled, then astounded. "Jess you're not ... ?" he cried.

"Of course not," she laughed at his expression. "But ... if we married ... "

'Married'. How wonderful it sounded, she thought.

"When, not if." He held her shoulders and stared into her face, smiling as if searching for something unexpected. "Is that what you'd really like?"

Jessie smiled. "I'm not sure ... but ...yes ... well ... perhaps ... we'll see."

CHAPTER FIFTEEN

Twelve days later, Archer Prince sat on his bed scribbling. The grimy counterpane was heaped with papers, more had cascaded to the floor. His thin shoulders were hunched and every few minutes he would raise his head and gaze wildly around the damp and extremely cold room, as if unsure where he was. His dark hair was unkempt, streaked with grey and clinging to the collar of his threadbare shirt. At last he finished his writing with a flourish. He stood.

"Sir," he read aloud, in a soft, menacing tone, "the next time I ask you for a reference will be at Bow Street Police Station." His voice rose. "It is there that my lawyer will expose you!" He seemed satisfied with this, a sneering smile playing over his features for a moment. Then his eyes went blank, his hand dropped to his side and the paper fluttered to join the others on the floor.

He took a long knife from the table and hacked at a stale loaf. While eating, he searched the pile of papers on the bed, turning it over frantically until he appeared suddenly to find what he was looking for. He spat out the last few crumbs and smoothed the letter, which was of good quality paper with a monogram and a coronet.

An expression, almost of reverence, transformed his thin features. He smoothed his moustache, swept back his lank hair, rose elegantly and bowed.

"His Grace the Duke of York," he read, "wishes to thank Mr Richard Archer Prince for his charming poem celebrating the birth of their son ... the birth of their son," he repeated. He began to move round the room with the peculiar, light-footed step he had affected on stage. He bowed again deeply.

"Your Royal Highness, may I present the celebrated actor, Richard Archer Prince. He has at last the chance he has so long deserved. Thank you, your Grace..." Suddenly his expression changed and he shouted, "Where is my writing then? I must have it returned immediately!"

There was a knock at the door. Prince froze. After a few moments the door was opened cautiously, and a small woman wearing a shawl and a thick, dark apron put her head round the door. Seeing Prince standing there she smiled nervously. "Mr Prince, sir?"

Prince bowed formally. "Ah, Mrs Darby," he said in a deep and ingratiating tone. "What an honour you do me, ma'am. A pleasant surprise, a very pleasant surprise indeed."

"How's that then, Mr Prince?" Mrs Darby looked wary.

"Why ... " began Prince. His face clouded. "I can't remember," he said vaguely.

There was a pause. Mrs Darby took a deep breath.

"I was grateful when you paid up, Mr Prince,` she said, kindly yet determined. "That I was ... but ... well, sir ... I'm afraid it's ... mounted up again, as you might say." She folded her thin arms and waited.

"How many weeks?" demanded Prince, suddenly lucid.

"Two, sir." She held his gaze. Her eyes were cold and watery.

"I have no money," said Prince simply. "What shall I do?"

Mrs Darby slid her hands into her apron pockets and shrugged. "I don't know, Mr Prince," she said. "I'm sorry for you but – you understand ... I must have my rent."

Archer Prince regarded her solemnly. Mrs Darby noted how thin and untidy he had become. Suddenly he took his cloak and greasy hat from the back of a chair, and picked up the knife, slipping it in the inside pocket of his threadbare jacket.

He smiled. "I shall go and see my sister, " he declared, airily. "I have high hopes of her, Mrs Darby, high hopes." He paused and turned. "If not," he said, the smile fading, "well, it will be one way or the other."

Mrs Darby looked puzzled. "What do you mean, sir?" she asked.

Archer Prince wrapped his cloak around him with a practised gesture and rammed the hat on his head.

"That, Mrs Darby," he oddly declared, "is best known to God or man."

Mrs Darby regarded her attic room with dismay as she heard his footsteps going down the stairs.

In response to a thunderous knocking, the clerk at the Actors' Benevolent Fund opened the door but, on seeing who waited there, did his best to close it again.

"I must see the Secretary," shouted Prince. "It's a matter of the utmost urgency."

"Mr Prince, I'm sorry sir," the clerk put all his weight against the door. "The secretary cannot see you."

"But the emergency committee..."

The clerk sighed. "The emergency committee cannot reconsider your case. Your application has already been rejected!"

"Rejected, was it?" snarled Prince. He breathed heavily as though contemplating violence. Then, abruptly, his manner changed. "Might I enquire the name of the Chairman on that occasion?" he asked politely. Surprised and relieved at this altered tone, the clerk paused. "Why ... ", his forehead wrinkled, "I believe it was Mr Terry, sir" he said, and closed the door.

"I believe it was Mr Terry, ... sir, Terry sir!" mocked Prince. "Mr Terry, sir – Terry sir ..." Suddenly the syllables blurred and the name became the one which had obsessed him for so long.

-Terriss! he muttered "Terriss!" He turned on his heel and walked into the street. How long he walked he didn't know. He called into an agency in Maiden Lane but as usual there was no work for him. He walked slowly down towards the Strand. A cold drizzle was falling. People hurried by, heads down.

Maggie Archer, wearing a new coat with a fox fur and a tight-fitting velvet hat was not pleased to see her half brother loom out of the shadows. She was on Abingdon's arm and would have crossed over but Prince was already hurrying towards them. 'God!, How awful he looked,' she thought. 'What a disgrace he was.'

"Good evening, Mr Abingdon, Maggie," Prince said urgently. "I wonder, sir – if you could oblige a fellow actor in distress?" Maggie bit her lip and turned her head away.

"Ah, Prince," said Abingdon loftily. "What still no engagement? How terribly unfair!"

"It would only be a temporary loan, sir," pleaded Prince. "I have the promise of … " his voice tailed away. He waited. He could smell the port on Abingdon's breath. It made him feel dizzy. Abingdon, his eyes bright, his face flushed, regarded him disdainfully. He pulled off an expensive glove and took a few coins from his pocket.

"Well … here you are," he said, "but," he smiled, thinly, " really this cannot go on you know. One wishes to be generous but … ahem …" he bowed and strode on, leaving Maggie.

Her face was tight with hatred. "I told you to get out o' London," she spat at him. "Just clear off, Archer and leave me alone. You'll ruin all my chances, you will."

"Just a few coppers, Maggie."

She stared at him. With his gaunt face, greasy hair and squinty eye -he was disgusting!

"I'm telling you, Archer," she said between clenched teeth, "I'd rather see you dead in the gutter than give you another farthing." She moved away. "And that's the truth!" she called, as she ran to catch up with Abingdon.

Jessie sat on her bed in tears. "I know it's stupid," she said, "but it's such a horrible dream. First of all I can't find you and then when I do, you keep on falling and I can't catch you ... and – and it keeps on coming back. That's the third time I've had the same dream. What does it mean?"

Will hugged her. "Nothing at all. " he said. "You're just thoroughly overwrought. We're both under a deal of strain. It will pass, dearest girl. Please do cheer up ... for me."

"Oh Will, I'm so sorry," Jessie hung her head. "You have so much more to cope with."

Will stroked her hair. "I know that, apart from the theatre, I've hardly seen you but..."

"Hush, " said Jessie. "How could I possibly begrudge her these hours with you? Dear heaven, what sort of woman would that make me?"

"I know exactly what sort of woman you are," said Will taking her hands and pulling her to her feet. "Brave and loving and ... I don't know what I'd do without you." He kissed the end of her nose and she smiled, and wiped her eyes.

"Harry wants a game of chess," he continued. "I'm not really in the mood but...."

"It will do you good," said Jessie, as they passed into the drawing room where Harry Graves, Will's godfather, and oldest friend, was already setting out the chess-board.

The three of them had dined together. Jessie had been surprised and delighted when they had arrived. She never knew when to expect her lover these days.

"I slipped into the Green Room Club on my way here," Will had announced, "and there was Harry."

"I always know there's something good to eat at Jessie's" said Harry Graves. "And as usual, that was an excellent dinner. Right, Will. Now you're due for a thrashing!"

Jessie watched them for a while then got to her feet.

"I'm going down to the theatre now," she said. "I need to see the Wardrobe Mistress. My sleeves are still a little too tight.

And I hate being rushed. Don't make him late, Harry."

"I'll be along directly," said Will, frowning over his move.

Jessie and Will both had keys to a special pass-door to the Adelphi in Maiden Lane. It was, in fact the private entrance for Queen Victoria, but it enabled the two leading players to enter and leave the theatre without using the Stage Door. Lottie was already waiting for Jessie in her dressing room which was directly above. As Jessie stepped down from her cab she saw Archer Prince standing opposite the door in Maiden Lane. For a moment she thought of giving him some money to avoid him bothering Will. She took a step towards him but he looked so unpleasant that she changed her mind and, to avoid him, instead of using the pass-door she went down the side alley to the Stage Door. Prince watched her go, his face impassive.

A short while later a cab stopped at the corner of Maiden Lane. Will and Harry Graves alighted, Will giving his old friend a hand down.

"Not as agile as I used to be," said Harry Graves.

"Nonsense!" said Will, as he paid.

"Thank you, Mr Terriss, sir," said the driver.

Archer Prince's eyes flickered. He raised his head and breathed deeply.

"That's a capital idea, Harry." said Will, as they moved forward together.

"I certainly think it's worth a try," Harry Graves smiled.

Above, in her dressing room, Jessie heard her lover put his key in the door and turn it, but then there were no expected footsteps.

Archer Prince who had been standing motionless for the last hour suddenly lunged forward. The knife already in his hand, he leapt across the road. In a wild release of energy he stabbed Will twice in the back, once in the left shoulder, the other thrust near the spine, the violence of the blows forcing Will almost to his knees. Graves, at first bewildered, mistakenly thought in the first instance that they were friendly gestures. As

Will turned in disbelief and rose to face his attacker he was met with a savage upward thrust which penetrated his heart

"My God! I am stabbed," he cried.

At the sudden silence, followed by shouts and cries for help, Jessie and Lottie raced down the stairs. Will, already bleeding profusely was leaning against the wall.

"Here are my keys, Lottie," he said. "Catch that man!"

Harry Graves hung onto Prince who made no attempt to flee. "What did you do it for?" he asked, appalled.

"He impeded my career," answered Prince dully. "He kept me out of work for ten years."

It was like a frenzied copulation for Prince. The orgasm over, he stood quite still, lifeless and drained, curiously calm; the bloody knife still dangling from his hand.

Will took a step forward towards the stairs, then slowly crumpled and began to slide down the wall. As he fell, Jessie caught him. He was heavy and Lottie steadied her as she sank to her knees, supporting Will against her body. Lottie stepped back, her hand over her mouth. The lovers clung to each other at the foot of the dusty stairs.

"Jess, Jess, I am stabbed," he whispered.

"Don't try to talk, Will. Somebody send for a doctor!. Oh God ! he's bleeding so." She rocked him in her arms. The crowd began to collect, fellow actors, dressers, the theatre manager, followed by doctors, policemen. Why would they do nothing? Why.. why? What were they all saying? The words swirled around her and made no sense. Jessie felt as though she was in a terrifying new melodrama and she hadn't learned her lines. It was all madness. And the blood! The blood was everywhere and real, horribly real. She heard herself scream. He couldn't die. Not now. They didn't understand. None of them understood. How could they? She and Will were going to Australia. Why were they all looking at her like that?

The nightmare which would haunt Jessie Millward for the rest of her life had begun.

CHAPTER SIXTEEN

On the morning after the murder, Tom Terriss took Jessie to see his father's body which lay in the mortuary of the nearby church of St Martin-in-the-Fields. Will looked beautiful in death, like palest marble; but Jessie, who had so often gazed upon her lover's face in sleep, knew that this time there was no-one there. As she put a small bunch of lilies of the valley on his cold hands, the horror of the previous day once more overwhelmed her. Remembering his warmth, his strong arms, his energy and his zest for life, her heart twisted with the pain she felt would never leave her.

Henry Irving returned from Bradford where he was touring in *Peter the Great*. He came at once to Jessie. He talked quietly about the play, and of his hopes for the future, for, in her limbo of shock and misery, Jessie could see no future. Ellaline Terriss, still recovering from the loss of her baby, sent a telegram to Jessie. Seymour came as often as he could. Will's sisters and brothers all called to offer comfort. In the close-knit circle of her own family and that of Will, Jessie found nothing but compassion, but as far as Victorian Society was concerned, she was in a very difficult position.

Early on the morning of the funeral she sat in her darkened drawing room, still holding Will's watch as she had done since the evening he was killed. A small, newly-lit fire flickered. A pile of black-edged letters lay on the piano. The room was scented by a bowl of lilies of the valley which stood before a picture of Will in an ornate silver frame. Lottie came in quietly with a tray. She put it down on the table and pulled back the curtains, leaving the blinds drawn.

"You can't go on sitting here in the dark, Miss Jessie," she said gently. "It won't do any good and ... and it's not healthy." Jessie made no sound.

"I've brought you up some hot milk," continued Lottie. "And see, Cook has made you some scones not ten minutes ago." She paused. "You must eat."

Jessie turned and shook her head, her face startlingly pale against the collar of her elaborate black dress, her eyes haunted. She shuddered.

"Not to-day, Lottie," she said falteringly, "not today."

"Well, at least try the milk," said Lottie, offering her the glass. Jessie refused.

"I went down early to see the wreath," said Lottie, with a cheerfulness she was far from feeling. "it's very beautiful. And so is mine. They've been working all night – same as every florist in London. They reckon there'll be more than a thousand wreaths." She sighed." He was well-loved and no mistake."

"And the one who loved him best in all the world has no place, Lottie," said Jessie bitterly. She paused. "They'd much prefer me to remain well out of sight," she added.

"That's nonsense, Miss Jessie ...."

"Nonsense, is it?" Jessie snatched up a newspaper. As she read she began to walk up and down.

"Dr Hayward Telegraphs please deny any mention of Miss Millward's name in connection with the death of Mr William Terriss ..." Jessie's hands shook.

"Miss Jessie don't"

"Dr Hayward may not have intended to mention the lady's name," continued Jessie with heavy sarcasm, *"and it is now obvious that he had no such intention ... in the interviews with Dr*

167

Hayward published in other papers, the Doctor did not mention 'the name' in all cases."

"You see Lottie. Not only would they like me to be invisible ... I am unmentionable as well.! My darling Will is dead and now he must be honoured by the Establishment ... with all its lies and empty pageantry. Oh yes," she began to cry. "You can be sure they will deny any mention of Miss Millward's name." She threw down the paper and picked up another. " And look here in the Telegraph.

"He left for the theatre from the green room club ... he was staying at the Cecil Hotel ... anything but the truth. I simply don't exist. It's so cruel ... "

"Hush ... hush," said Lottie as she took the papers and led Jessie back to her chair.

"Oh, Lottie," said Jessie, her sobs quietening. "I loved him so."

"I know, Miss Jessie, I know."

"We knew we could never marry while ... Oh God, poor Isabel!" Jessie crossed her arms onto her shoulders and rocked herself back and forth. " I have been truly punished for all my wicked desires ... "

"Hush, " said Lottie. "Let me brush your hair." Lottie unpinned Jessie's long dark hair and began to brush it with soothing expertise. Jessie's eyes closed and she became calmer.

"Lottie, " she said tremulously. "Don't ever leave me."

"What an idea," said Lottie, brushing slowly. "I'll never leave you. Although," she began, seeing a chance to distract Jessie, "that wasn't what I thought when I first came. I thought this was a funny old place I'd tumbled into and no mistake. Do you remember?"

Jessie nodded.

"That very first day I arrived and Cook told me to tell you that luncheon was served and I opened the drawing room door and there was you on your knees in front of Mr Terriss. "SPARE THIS MAN'S LIFE " you was shouting. It really upset me."

Jessie gave a small smile and, encouraged, Lottie continued. "I went down and told Cook I did. 'You've been here longer than me' I said 'And I think you ought to be told. There's a strange man in the drawing room with Miss Jessie and she's on her knees askin' him to save some man's life and by the look of him I don't think he's going to do it."

Jessie squeezed Lottie's hand. "Poor Lottie," she said. "You must have found it all very bewildering."

Lottie smiled. "Well – it was certainly different from my other place. And when I found we was to dine at four o'clock in the afternoon and then we had to go off to the theatre ... "

"Ah yes," said Jessie. "The theatre. How suspicious you were. I wasn't sure you'd ever get used to it."

"We all have our different duties in life," said Lottie pinning up Jessie's hair. "There that's better ... and yours at this moment Miss, is to drink up this milk before it's cold."

Jessie gave in and drank slowly while Lottie watched over her. She handed her the glass and picked up Will's watch again. She opened the back. "See Lottie," she said sadly, "That's how I looked on the day we first met. Fifteen years ago. Fifteen years."

She shook her head." It's just as well we can't look into the future isn't it ... ? That day was one of the happiest of my life." She paused and closed the watch. "How am I going to get through this day, Lottie?" she asked. "I'm not sure I can face it".

Lottie looked at her mistress. She hesitated. "Are you quite sure about going? I don't want you being hurt any more, Miss Jessie," she said. "But ... you know best."

The door bell rang. Lottie left the room and returned with Sir Henry Irving.

"My dear Jessie," he handed her a bunch of violets.

She buried her face in their scented freshness, then laid them on the table. Irving took her hands and kissed them.

"My dear child, " he said. "You are so cold. Come nearer the fire." He moved the chairs and they sat for a moment in silence.

Henry Irving looked at her compassionately. "I have just taken the Queen's condolences to Bedford Park, " he said. "That is my duty done to the Terriss family. Now I can be with you. We have a little while yet."

"You are very kind," said Jessie. "I fear I'm poor company."

How small she looked, he thought, more like a hurt child than a famous actress. "We must strive to cheer each other on this saddest of days," he said. "Poor Will, how I shall miss him. The whole of London is stunned. There have been crowds outside Bedford Park all weekend. And already the streets are thickly-lined. He was well-loved."

"I think he would have been surprised," said Jessie. "Oh, he knew he was popular of course but ... he felt that his present work was of little value ... compared to those days at the Lyceum."

"No-one could bring such reality, such life to the melodrama," said Irving, smiling.

Jessie undid the watch and showed him her picture.

"I gave him this," she said, "just before I returned to America... after that first tour with you."

Irving looked at it with a rueful smile. "I thought I was doing the right thing when I did my best to protect you," he said. "But ... in the end I was powerless."

"We were all powerless," said Jessie simply.

Irving leaned back in his chair. "How well I remember you in *Much Ado*," he said. "You were the perfect choice for Hero. Ellen was doubtful at first but ..."

"She was so kind," said Jessie, impulsively. "I learned so much from her. And ... how naïve and unskilled I must have seemed."

"Your naïveté, your youth and freshness, were the qualities I wanted," said Irving. "Undisciplined you certainly were, Miss Millward," his eyes flashed with amusement, "But you were not unskilled and you learned very quickly."

Jessie sat in silence. Then she spoke quietly, as if to herself.

"Take my hand," Will said, on that first day – "And you will have a friend for life," her voice trembled. She looked up at Irving. "Sometimes when I couldn't sleep – when I was studying a new part, I would wonder about the future. Whether he would tire of me," she smiled briefly. "I thought at first he was bound to, " she said. "But ... but when I began to hope and then to believe that our love was strong and lasting I would sometimes imagine myself caring for him as he grew older ... "

"My dear," said Irving gently. "He would have hated being old. He was so vigorous, so youthful still...."

"But to die so cruelly..." Jessie burst out. "So senselessly! And for what?"

"It was the act of a madman," said Irving. "We must remember that. It is to your work, Jessie, that you must now turn to sustain you."

Jessie shook her head. "I shall never work again," she said harshly." I am empty. I have nothing to give ... or to live for."

"You feel that now," said Irving. "But ... in the end ... it is only the great demands of our profession that enable us to transcend all personal anguish. We can transmute them into our very work ... "

"I don't believe it!" cried Jessie passionately. "Death makes a mockery of play-acting. All those tears I've shed onstage mean nothing... nothing." She began to weep and turned her head away, stroking her throat. "No-one can understand..." she choked.

"You are wrong." Irving got slowly to his feet. He walked to the piano, picked up the violets he had brought her and for a moment held them to his face. "It is almost thirty years ago, Jessie," he said quietly, but with great intensity. "But the scent of violets can still make me catch my breath." He returned to her side and from his wallet took a faded photograph.

"You see," he said. " I too carry a picture close to my heart." He handed it to Jessie. "I've never shown this to a living soul save you," he said.

Jessie, surprised, took the photograph and looked at the girlish face, the sweet mouth, the soft curling fringe high on the forehead, the heavy-lidded eyes, the delicate eyebrows. "She's very beautiful, " she said.

"When she died," said Irving, his voice suddenly strained, "without my work I would have lost my reason. And for me Jessie, there were no years of a loving partnership to remember … only misunderstandings and bitterness." He paused.

"How did she die?" asked Jessie.

"She had scarlet fever," answered Irving. "It was very sudden." He sighed. "Afterwards ... in my loneliness and misery I married unwisely but ... that is all one now, but," he turned to her fiercely, "it was my work, my work, Jessie that has been my life and my soul's balm. And it will be so for you … if you will let it." He took her hands in his. "Promise me that you will try."

Jessie looked into the eyes of the great actor. She knew so well that unique face which could express every emotion from the most noble melancholy to the most impish humour. How many times that intense scrutiny had scared her. At the Lyceum, on tour in America, and, even when she was a child, so long ago, listening in fascinated terror to his fireside recitations. Now there was nothing in those eyes but a compelling tenderness.

"I promise," she said. "And … thank you."

Irving pulled out his watch and rose to his feet.

"It is time, Jessie," he said. "time for our final performance. You and I ...and Will." he waited. "Are you ready?"

Jessie sat motionless. "I do so want to, but ... " she hesitated. "How can I go to Brompton?" she said at last, looking up at him. "The unmentionable Miss Millward?"

"Courage, Jessie," said Irving, taking her by the hand. "Unmentionable in some circles perhaps ... but what of them?" He gently pulled her to her feet. "I see no reason why you should be invisible as well. It is your right and ... I am quite sure he would have wished it."

"Oh," said Jessie. "Yes. I would like to go. To be near my beloved Will."

"Then ring for Lottie, and let us be off," said Irving. "Seymour will travel with us. He will be downstairs by now."

Since early morning many hundreds had gathered outside the Terriss family home in Bedford Park. They watched as one florist's van after another delivered a stream of elaborate wreaths to the house. Other wreaths arrived with the open hearse pulled by four splendid black plumed horses. As the coffin was carried out all heads were bowed in sad respect. Two more hearses, completely laden with flowers, followed the coffin before the cortège of eleven mourning coaches and more than thirty private carriages, assembled and moved off.

The sad procession made its way at walking pace three and a half miles through the streets of West London. The sky was grey and as they reached Turnham Green station where Will had been a well-known fellow passenger, as many as ten thousand people stood in the bitterly cold wind to see him pass by.

Young Bob, still in the ticket office, but now a married man with greying sideboards, cried unashamedly as he clutched his railway hat to his chest. At Hammersmith Broadway the streets were packed and all down the Warwick Road to Brompton Cemetery the waiting crowds stood in silent grief, a ripple of hats being removed and replaced as the coffin went by. By the time the procession had reached the cemetery over fifty thousand ordinary people had braved the cold to pay their respects to one of the country's most popular actors, shock and sorrow on every face.

It was a sea of such faces that greeted Jessie. As they drew level with the brick arches of the cemetery and she glimpsed the crowds inside the railings her heart began to thud and she kept her head bowed. The carriage passed under the great arch of the North entrance and came to a halt. Brompton Cemetery is dramatic in its very concept. The wide, central avenue, almost three-quarters of a mile long, leads to parallel colonnades which open out into a great circle, beyond which is the lead-domed, octagonal chapel. The architect, Benjamin Baud, had assisted with the rebuilding of Windsor Castle and had based his designs for Brompton Cemetery on the basilica of St Peter's in Rome.

For such an important funeral, the public were restricted to one area from where they could watch the arrival of the crowd of official mourners who lined the long central avenue. Tall lime trees standing sentinel along its whole length stretched their bare branches overhead. The side avenues were packed with carriages. Irving's carriage was sighted and a ripple ran through the crowd and all heads turned. As he alighted and they watched him reach up to help Jessie, an audible frisson went through the rows of very cold, top-hatted, frock-coated gentlemen.

Victorian funerals were a male affair. Even respectable women were a rarity. This woman – famous actress though she might be – was today cast as ' the Mistress'. As such, the feeling was evident, she should have had the decency to stay where Mistresses belonged on such an occasion: out of sight. Jessie, sensing such hostility, faltered.

"I don't think this is wise," she whispered to Irving. "It will cause a scandal."

Irving took her hand in a firm grasp. "I see little point in my having accepted a knighthood," he said, calmly. "if it precludes my behaving in a chivalrous manner." He handed her down from the carriage, bowed, and gave her a dazzling smile. "Today, " he said. "You do me the great honour of accepting me as your champion." As he took her arm, Seymour moved to her other side. "Chin up, Jess," he said, quietly.

Will was to be buried in his mother's grave by the east wall, and Irving and Seymour walked quietly on the lower path nearby with Jessie, while the cortége arrived and the coffin was carried into the chapel, with its tall, ornate domed room. The area surrounding the grave seemed to defy the December weather, bursting into bloom as it was rapidly covered with the many hundreds of wreaths. The family service was so brief that the last carriages of the cortège had hardly driven through the gates before the coffin was born to the graveside, accompanied by three priests and Will's sons, brothers and cousins.

With perfect timing, Irving moved forward with Jessie and she and Seymour took their place. As the committal began Jessie hardly listened. She felt removed from all the hostile glances. She found herself remembering so many things. Will, making her laugh at rehearsals, climbing through her window with his face streaked with dirt, kissing her under the tree in the snow, dressing up as his famously rich 'sister' on board ship, pruning the roses at Jessamine Cottage. These memories belonged to her alone.

The words ended. Following the family, she moved forward and gently threw the lilies of the valley onto the coffin. Now she had to turn and face the crowd. Yet with Irving and Seymour beside her it seemed as though Will himself were also there, giving her courage as he had always done. They began to walk forward toward a vast, unending, black-coated throng.

"Remember what I taught you," said Irving, softly "Head high, Jessie, and straight back. "

The famous actor bowed, smiling acknowledgements to either side as they slowly walked up the long central avenue. "And as for them, " he said quietly to Jessie, "Let them talk! Let them all talk!"

EPILOGUE

At his trial on Friday January 14 1898, Richard Archer Prince was found guilty but insane. He spent the next forty years in Broadmoor Asylum.

A few months after Terriss's funeral, his wife, Isabel, died of cancer.

In July 1898 the Duchess of Devonshire laid the foundation stone in Eastbourne for

'A Life-boat House to be built in the memory of William Terriss, with subscriptions received by the Daily Telegraph from those who loved and admired him, and who sorrowed together with all his friends and fellow countrymen at his most cruel and untimely end.'

The Lifeboat House has since become a Life-Boat Museum and Terriss's picture hangs among those of many courageous lifeboat men. He would, I am sure, be proud to be among such company.

Mr W. Abingdon, confronted by several actors who accused him of causing the death of Will Terriss, left England for America. At first he prospered and married well but the marriage did not last, his fortunes changed and, in 1918, he cut his throat.

After a year of travelling in Italy, Jessie kept her promise to Irving and returned to work, but not to the English stage. She went to America for Charles Frohman and continued to act successfully for some fifteen years. In middle age she discovered a talent for playing comedy which she had had no opportunity to develop in her youth.

Ten years after Terriss's murder she married a fellow actor, John Glendinning. Although a Scot, Glendinning had worked in America for many years, but as a young man he had toured England playing all the heroes of melodrama. He had even been billed as 'the Terriss of the Road'. They both returned to England in 1913 but Jessie was once more alone when her husband died three years later. She moved to a flat in West Kensington where she lived quietly.

In 1930 a Daily Express special correspondent wrote ...

'In Brighton tonight I saw a great actress playing her last great drama – waiting for the final curtain. She is Jessie Millward, one of the best-loved actresses of the Victorian stage, and William Terriss's leading lady in all his melodramas, who is lying dangerously ill in a nursing home here. She had been living in a small hotel, alone and in failing health. She spoke of her London audiences and of the death of William Terriss who was murdered at the stage door and died in her arms ... "She was so ill on Saturday evening," said Miss Florence Millward, her younger sister, "that we thought she could not live until the morning. But her wonderful will overcame her illness and somehow she rallied. She is terribly weak but her mind is as clear as ever. Tonight she spoke of her first love affair, which I am not old enough even to remember."'

Florence Millward was twenty five years old when Terriss was murdered! Was she merely being coy about her age or reluctant, even in 1930, to talk about Jessie and Will?

Shortly after Terriss's murder, George Bernard Shaw wrote to Ellen Terry. He and Terriss had resolved their differences over *The Devil's Disciple*.

'My calculations are quite put out by the unforeseen extinction of Terriss,' he wrote. 'I was scheming to get him the part, with Jessie as Judith. Poor Terriss, I'll miss him. Now he is only a name and a bunch of lies in the newspaper.'

Even then, Shaw scorned the humbug.

The centenary of William Terriss's murder in December 1987 was rightly celebrated with the unveiling of a plaque at the scene of the crime. This was, of course, Terriss's day but there was no mention of Jessie. The renowned actor Sir Donald Sinden spoke eloquently of the crime, even brandishing the knife with which Terriss was stabbed. However, an interesting talk was given at the Theatre Museum by Frances Hughes and Jessie was, at last, included. Celebrations were also held at the Green Room Club.

Since my interest in this story I have been approached several times by men who claim to be 'fans of Terriss'. When, however, I explain that my story also appreciates his relationship with Jessie Millward, strangely, I hear no more. On the day of the centenary I was in the bar of the C.A.A, the London club for Acts and Actors in Bedford Street. A member of the Green Room club bought me a drink.

"You realise, Ruth," he said, "that in Terriss's day the Green Room Club was in this very building."

Having been a member of the C.A.A. for many years I was surprised at my ignorance and intrigued.

"Yes," my host continued, "it was from this very spot that poor Terriss left to go down to the theatre on that fateful night."

"Actually ... no," I murmured. "He'd been playing chess with Harry Graves and they had both dined at Jessie's."

He looked at me long and hard. He tapped the side of his nose with a finger and said, conspiratorially, "We don't talk about that."

So, even after a hundred years, the whiff of Victorian rectitude remains.

Why, today, loving Jessie Millward is still seen by some to diminish the bright hero, William Terriss, is incomprehensible to me.

Happily, not everyone feels that way. I recently had the great pleasure of meeting William Terriss's great, great granddaughter, Lucia Stuart. She is astonishingly like Ellaline, and has warmly approved the book.

In August 1892 Terriss persuaded Jessie that she ought to make a will. They had been touring together all over England and America and another long, arduous tour with Irving was planned for the following year. This was her letter to him.

"My darling Will,

I have left everything I possess to my mother and I hope that you will think I have done right. I should like you to have a souvenir; take what ever you wish. Believe me my lover, if I could have my life all over again I should only wish it to be with you. I have never regretted the love I have given you, and I thank you for all your love and goodness to me. I die as I have lived, loving you, my beloved,

Jessie.

I would like to feel that this book, in some small way, honours them both.

BIBLIOGRAPHY

Myself and Others. Jessie Millward. (Hutchinson 1923)

The Life of William Terriss. Arthur J Smythe (Constable 1898)

William Terriss & Richard Prince. GeorgeRowell. (Society for Theatre Research.1987)

Henry Irving, The Actor and his World. Laurence Irving. (Faber & Faber) 1951

Personal Reminiscences of Henry Irving. Bram Stoker.

Story of my Life. Ellen Terry.

Ellen Terry. Nina Auerbach. (Orion)

Between Ourselves. Seymour Hicks. (Cassell,1930)

Just a little bit of String. Ellaline Terriss.(Hutchinson 1955)

Impressions of America. Joseph Hatton.

A few Memories. Mary Anderson.

The Gaiety Years Alan Hyman.

A Nursery in the Nineties. Eleanor Fargeon

Actresses as Working Women. Tracy Davis (Performing Arts 1991)

Empty Chairs. Squire Bancroft.(John Murray 1925)

Newspapers and Journals of the period.